Once Upon a Time in Ghostly Japan

装幀 ● 菊地信義
装画 ● 愛企画センター

まんが日本昔ばなし 妖^{あや}しのお話

Once Upon a Time in Ghostly Japan

川内彩友美［編］

ラルフ・マッカーシー［訳］

Bilingual **B**ooks

まんが日本昔ばなし
妖しのお話

Once upon a time
in *Ghostly* Japan

目次

鶴の恩返し

10

雪女

26

舌切り雀

40

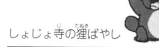
しょじょ寺の狸ばやし

60

Contents

The Gratitude of the Crane

11

The Snow Woman

27

The Sparrow's Tongue

41

The Tanuki Band of Shojoji

61

耳なし芳一
78

分福茶釜
94

赤ん坊になったおばあさん
110

おいてけ堀
126

Earless Ho-ichi

79

Bunbuku Teakettle

95

Baby Grandma

111

Leave Them and Go

127

鶴の恩返し

む かしむかし、あるところ に、心のやさしいおじい さんとおばあさんが住んでおり ましたそうな。

ある日のこと、おじいさんが 山でしばかりをしての帰り道、 沼のあたりでつるの鳴きさけぶ声 が聞こえました。

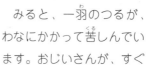

みると、一羽のつるが、 わなにかかって苦しんでい ます。おじいさんが、すぐ につるを助けだすと、 つるはよろこびを羽 いっぱいにあらわし て、雪の空へと飛び 去っていきました。

The Gratitude of the Crane

Once upon a time a kindhearted old man lived with his wife in a little house deep in the woods. The old couple were happy with their simple, quiet life, although it did get a bit lonely at times. They often thought how nice it would be if only they had a child of their own.

One day, as usual, the old man went out to gather firewood in the mountains near his home. He was on his way back that evening when he heard what sounded like a cry for help. He followed the sound to a frozen marsh by the side of the road. And there he found a beautiful white crane with its leg caught in a hunter's trap. The old man got down on his knees and opened the trap to set the crane free. It flapped its wings, cried out for joy, and flew off into the snow-filled sky.

その日の夜、いろりのそばでおじいさんは、今日のできごとをおばあさんに話しておりました。

「それはそれは、うれしそうじゃった。」

やさしいおばあさんもにっこりして、なんだか二人は、とても幸せな気分になりました。

そのときです。

とんとん、とんとん。

だれかがたずねてきたではありませんか。だれでしょう。こんな夜ふけに。

しかも、雪の夜に……。

とんとん、とんとん。

おじいさんはふしぎに思いながら、そっと戸を開けてみますと——、なんと、雪の中に、かわいい娘が立っているではありませんか。

旅のとちゅうで、道に迷ったというのです。

やさしいおじいさんとおばあさんは、よろこんで娘をとめてあげようと、家に招き入れました。

おばあさんは、あたたかいおかゆを作って食べさせてやりました。

That night, sitting before the fire, the old man told his wife what had happened. "How happy that crane looked!" he chuckled. The old woman smiled, and they sat chatting idly and thinking pleasant thoughts until it was time to go to bed. They were about to do just that when someone knocked at the front door.

Knock, knock. Knock, knock.

Who could it be so late at night, so deep in the woods, and with all that snow outside?

Knock, knock.

The old man went to the door and opened it. And there,

to his astonishment, stood a lovely young maiden.

"Forgive me for disturbing you, sir," she said. "But I seem to have lost my way…"

"Come inside, child. My goodness, you must be freezing!" The old man asked his wife to prepare a bowl of hot rice gruel, and offered the girl a seat near the fire. "You'd better stay here tonight," he told her. "We've plenty of room."

「ほんとうにありがとうござい
ました。」

　話を聞いてみると、この娘には
行くあてがないというのです。

　おじいさんがやさしくいいまし
た。

　「のう、娘さんや、それならわ
しらといっしょにくらしなされ。」

　そうじゃ、そうじゃというように、おばあさんもう
なずきます。

　「わたしもこんなうれしいことはございません。よろ
しくおねがいします。」

　娘は二人に頭を下げました。

　「おう、そうかそうか。」

　おじいさんとおばあさんも頭を下げました。

　子どものいないおじいさんとおばあさんにとって、
こんなうれしいことはありません。その夜は、三人で
ゆっくりとねむりました。

　さて、明けがたにはまだ闇がある暗いうちに、娘は
そっと起きだしました。

　おじいさん、おばあさんが目をさま
さないように、そうっと台所におりて
いきます。

　おじいさん、おばあさんのために朝
ごはんのしたくをしようと、娘は米び

"Oh, thank you, sir," said the girl. "You're very kind."

The old woman served the gruel and waited until the girl had eaten it before asking, "Where are you traveling to, miss?"

"Well…" The girl hesitated. "I haven't really decided yet."

A mere girl, traveling all alone with nowhere to go? She must have met with some great misfortune, thought the old man. He felt sorry for her and told her she was welcome to stay with him and his wife for as long as she liked. They'd be glad, he said, for the help and companionship.

"Do you really mean it?" cried the girl. "Oh, that would be wonderful! I'd like very much to stay with you."

"Well, then, it's settled," the old man said. "Now let's get some sleep. We can talk more in the morning."

The old couple slept very well indeed that night. They were still snoring softly when the girl got up, well before dawn, and went to the kitchen. She wanted to have breakfast ready for them when they awoke. But every barrel and cupboard she looked in

つをのぞいたのですが……、からっぽです。お米もおみそもありません。

　そのとき、娘は糸のたばを見つけました。なにを思ったのか、娘は糸のたばを持ってはた織りべやへ入っていきました。

　やがて、しめきったへやからは、きいとんから、きいとんから、という布を織るはた織りの音が聞こえてきました。

　朝の光がさしこんできました。

　おじいさん、おばあさんも目をさまし、となりの娘のねどこを見ましたが、もう娘のすがたはありません。

　そこへ、反物を持って娘が入ってきました。

　「なんと美しい布じゃ……。」

　「ほんに、美しい布じゃ……。」

　おじいさんとおばあさんは、反物を手にぽかーんとしています。

　「どうぞ、これを売ってお米やおみそなど、いりようなものを買ってきてください。」

　おじいさんは、大よろこびでその布をもって町へ売りにいきました。

　布は高い値段で売れました。

　おじいさんは、そのお金でお米やみそを買い、娘にはかわいいくしを買っておみやげにしました。

was bare. There wasn't a grain of rice or a pinch of miso to be found.

What she did find, however, was a basket filled with spools of thread. She took this and disappeared into the workroom next to the kitchen, closing the door behind her. Soon from behind the closed door came the sound of a loom.

Creak, tap, clack… Creak, tap, clack… Creak, tap, clack…

The old man and woman awoke shortly after sunrise and saw that the girl wasn't in her bed. Before they even had a chance to wonder what had happened to her, however, she appeared in the doorway, carrying a thick roll of woven brocade.

"What beautiful cloth!" exclaimed the old man.

"Yes, it really is lovely," the old woman agreed. She took the brocade in her hands and marveled at its wonderful design.

"I made it for you," said the girl. "Please take it and sell it. Then buy some rice and miso, and anything else you might need."

The old man was delighted. He took the brocade to town that morning and sold it for a very good price. With the money he bought lots of food and a pretty comb for the girl. That night,

その夜は、ほんとに幸せな夜でした。

　「さあ、楽しい夢でも見ようかの。」

　「おじいちゃんは、お休みください。わたしはもうひと仕事します。」

　そういう娘におじいさんはびっくり。

　「いかん、いかん。今夜はもうお休み。」

　「いいえ、わたしはおじいちゃんたちに、あの布を織ってあげたいの。いいでしょう。

　そのかわり、たった一つだけおねがいがあります。わたしがはたを織っているところを、けっして見ないでください。」

　「なに？　見てはならんと……。」

　「はい、やくそくしてください。」

　娘の顔には、なにやらひっしのようすがありました。

　おじいさんとおばあさんは、わけもわからず、ただうなずくだけでした。

　こうして娘は、夜ごとあの美しい布を一反ずつ織りあげていきました。

　それをおじいさんが町へ持っていくと、飛ぶように売れました。

　しかし、三日、五日とたつうちに、娘はだんだんやつれて元気がなくなっていきました。

after a delicious dinner, the three of them chatted contentedly by the fire.

"Well," said the old man when it had grown quite late, "why don't we turn in? We're sure to have sweet dreams tonight."

"Please go ahead," said the girl. "I have a bit more work to do."

"Oh no you don't. You've got to get your rest, child."

"I'm fine, really. I only want to weave a little more cloth for you." The girl looked down at her delicate white hands. "But I have a favor to ask. I want you to promise you'll never open the door to the workroom when I'm in there."

"Hm? You don't want us to see you weaving?"

"That's right. Please promise."

The old man and woman were puzzled by this odd request. But the girl was so insistent that finally they gave their word not to disturb her while she worked.

Each night from then on, the girl would weave a roll of beautiful brocade. And each day the old

　戸口に立って夕日をながめる娘のすがたはいまにもたおれそうでした。

　「せめて、あと一反織ってあげたい。」
　娘はそう考えていたのです。

　その日の夕食どきでした。おじいさんが町で買ってきたごちそうにも、娘は、すこしも手をつけません。

　「さ、もっとおたべ。」

　「いえ、もういいんです、もうひと仕事してきます。」
　これにはおじいさんもびっくり。

　「いかん！　今夜は休まにゃ体にどくじゃ。むりするんじゃない。」

　おじいさんがとめるのも聞かず、娘は、よろよろと立ち上がりました。

　「ほれそんなに弱ってしまって。」

　立ち上がってとめようとするおじいさんに、娘ははっきりした声でいいました。

　「もう一反だけ。」

　それを聞くと、なぜか二人は娘をとめることもできず、ただ、ただ娘の身を案じて、どうすることもできません。

　娘が仕事べやに入ると、戸はぴしゃりとしまりました。

　おじいさんとおばあさんは、ねどこに入っても心配でねむれません。

man would take the cloth to town and sell it at an excellent price. Soon there was enough rice and miso in the old couple's kitchen to last for months.

But with each passing day the girl grew paler and thinner. One evening the old man noticed her sitting by the open door, gazing wearily at the setting sun. She looked as if she might collapse at any moment. And later, at dinner, she hardly touched her food at all.

"Eat, child. You've got to eat…"

"I've had enough, thank you. There's a little more work I want to do."

"You're overdoing it, dear," said the old woman. "You have to rest. It's not good for you to work so hard."

But the girl wouldn't listen. She stood up, swaying, to leave the table.

"Look how weak you've become!" cried the old man. He rose to stop her, but the girl shook her head and looked deep into his eyes.

"Just one more roll," she said, and walked unsteadily into the workroom, closing the door behind her.

That night, the old couple were so worried about the girl that they couldn't get to sleep.

「おじいさん、なんかはたの音が弱って乱れてきたようじゃ……。」

「よし、見てこよう。」

おじいさんは、がばっとねどこから起き上がりました。

「娘とのやくそくが！」

おばあさんがとめましたが、おじいさんは娘のことが心配でなりません。

おじいさんは、仕事べやの戸を、そうっと開けて、中をのぞきました。

「あ、あ～～っ！」

なんと、はたを織っていたのは、娘ではなく一羽のつるでした。

つるは、自分の体から羽根をぬくとそれを布に織りこんでいました。

最後の力をふりしぼって、一本、また一本……。つるは、すっかり弱っておりました。

おじいさんは、こんどは戸をがらっと開けました。

はっと、気がついたつるは、しだいに娘のすがたに変わっていきました。

「お、おまえは。」

おどろくおじいさんの前に、娘は首をうなだれていいました。

「はい、わたしはあのとき助けられたつるでございます。」

"Dear," whispered the old woman. "Listen to the loom. It sounds... different tonight, somehow. I have a feeling something's very wrong."

The old man had the same feeling. "I'm going to have a look," he said, getting up.

"You can't do that, dear. You promised her..." But the old man was too concerned about the girl to let the promise stop him. He tiptoed to the workroom, opened the door a crack, and peered inside.

"Good heavens!" he gasped.

Sitting before the loom was a slender white crane. As the old man watched, the crane plucked one of its own feathers and carefully wove it into the cloth. Trembling, the bird was about to take hold of another feather when the old man flung open the door. The startled crane noticed him now for the first time and, right before his unbelieving eyes, slowly began transforming back into the lovely young maiden.

"You... You're..."

The girl hung her head and said, "Yes. I'm the crane you set free."

「あ、あのときの……つる……。」

「はい、命を助けていただいた恩がえしをしようと、一度だけ人間のすがたになることをゆるされて、ここにまいったのです。」

そういうと、娘はすーっと戸口のほうへ出ていきました。

「わたしはもう、ここにいることはできないのです。いつまでも、おじいちゃんたちの娘でいたかったわ……。」

そういって、外へ出た娘は、つるのすがたに変わって、ゆっくりと空へ飛びたっていきました。

「娘や、わたしたちのことをわすれないでおくれ。」

おじいさんは、祈るようにあの娘のくしをつるに投げました。

つるは、くしをくちばしで受け、二人にわかれをおしむように、一声二声鳴くと、どことも知れず冬の空高く飛び去っていきました。

（おわり）

"Ah! That night in the marsh…"

"Yes. You saved my life. I wanted to repay you somehow. But now that you've discovered my secret…" The girl ran out of the workroom to the front door. "I must go. I wish I could stay forever, but…"

With a sad glance back at the old man, the girl dashed out across the yard. And as she ran, she turned once again into a beautiful white crane. Spreading her wings, she lifted off gracefully into the night sky.

"Remember us, child! Don't ever forget us!" the old man called after her. "We love you!" He reached for the comb he had bought the girl, ran outside, and threw it into the air.

The crane circled back, caught the comb in her beak, and uttered a sorrowful cry of parting. Then she rose higher in the sky and vanished amid the moonlit clouds.

雪女

　　　かしむかしの、寒い寒い北国
む　でのお話です。あるところに、茂作と巳之吉というきこりの親子がすんでいましたそうな。

　この親子、山々がすっぽり雪につつまれるころになると、てっぽうをもって猟にでかけていくのです。

　ある日のこと、親子はいつものように雪山へ入っていきましたが、この日はおもうようにえものが見つかりません。

　そして、いつのまにか、空は黒雲におおわれ、冬山は人をよせつけぬかのようにあれはじめました。

　ふきすさぶ雪と風は、のぼってきた道も足あともかききけしてしまいます。

　二人は、やっときこり小屋をみつけて、そこであらしが去るのを待つことにしました。

The Snow Woman

Long ago in a small village in the cold, cold north country, a woodcutter named Mosaku lived with his son, Minokichi.

One freezing winter's morning, when the snow was too deep for cutting wood, Mosaku and Minokichi went hunting. They spent the entire day trudging through the mountains without spotting even so much as a rabbit. It was already late afternoon when, quite suddenly, great dark clouds rolled over the sky and snow began to fall, covering up the path and erasing the hunters' footprints behind them.

Although they could hardly see where they were going, they were lucky enough to stumble upon a woodcutters' hut. They decided to stay there until the storm blew over.

「今夜はここでとまるより、しかたあるめえ。」

「うんだな……。」

二人は、冬山のきびしさをだれよりも知っていました。

ちろちろともえる、いろりの火にあたりながら、山の夜をすごします。

茂作は、ごろりと横になりながら、巳之吉にこんなことを話しかけます。

「なあ、巳之吉……、おまえもそろそろ、よめをとらんといかんのう。わしは、はよう孫の顔が見とうなったわ。」

巳之吉は、だまってうなずいておりました。

そして、二人はひるまのつかれからか、いつのまにかねむりこんでしまったのです。

小屋の外はふぶきです。風が戸をたたきます。風のいきおいで、戸ががたんと開き、雪がまいこんできました。

いろりの火が、ふっと消えました。

「うー、寒い……。」

あまりの寒さに、巳之吉は目をさましました。

そのとき、巳之吉は見たのです。雪のまう土間に人影を──。

"We may have to spend the night here," said Mosaku as he stacked some wood in the fireplace.

"I'm afraid so, Father."

The two men sat talking beside the flickering fire while the wind howled around the door. It had been a long time since they'd had a good heart-to-heart talk, and the hours went quickly by. It was already quite late when Mosaku lay down on the floor facing his son.

"You know, son," he said, "when a man gets to be my age, he begins to want grandchildren. Isn't it time you thought about getting married?"

Minokichi blushed and stared dreamily at the fire. Little did he know that those were the last words his poor father would ever speak…

They were both very tired from their long day, and soon they were fast asleep. Outside, the snowstorm continued to rage. It was after midnight when an especially strong gust of wind suddenly blew the door ajar. Snow came swirling into the hut, putting out the fire.

Minokichi woke up shivering. "Brrr! It's f-freezing," he muttered, sitting up. That's when he saw her. She was standing in the shadows just inside the open door.

「だ、だ、だれじゃ、そこに
おるのは。」

　人影はすがたをあらわしまし
た。すきとおるようなはだの、
うつくしい女の人でしたが、そ
のひとみのなんとつめたいこと。

　雪女です！

　雪女は、ねむっている茂作の
足もとに立つと、口から白い息
をはきだしました。

　女は雪の精なのでしょうか。
その寒さで、茂作をつつみこみました。

　茂作の顔に白い息がかかると、茂作のからだはだん
だんと白くかわっていきます。そして、ねむったよう
に、しずかに息をひきとっていきました。

　巳之吉は、両手で顔をおおいました。

　なんとおそろしいことでしょう！　目のまえで、父
親のからだがつめたくなっていったのですから。

　雪女は、こんどは巳之吉のほうへ近づいてきます。

「た、た、たすけてくれ！」

　ひっしでにげようとする巳之吉に、なぜか雪女はや
さしい表情を見せました。

　「見たところ、そなたはまだ若々しく、うつくしい
のちが輝いています。たすけてあげましょう。生きぬ
くのです。」

"Who is it? Who's there?"

Out of the shadows stepped a beautiful woman dressed in flowing white silk. Her hair was long and black, and her skin was as pale and smooth as polished ivory. But as he looked into her cold, dark eyes, Minokichi felt a shiver run down his spine.

The woman ignored him, however, and walked slowly toward his father, who was still asleep. Minokichi watched helplessly as the woman bent down and exhaled a frosty white cloud that hung over Mosaku like a hungry ghost.

"Father!" he cried, trembling with fear. "Father!" But there was no response. The woman turned and moved toward Minokichi.

"Help! Help!" Minokichi stood up to run, but the woman stepped in front of him, blocking his path. She stared deep into his eyes and, to his horror and bewilderment, her cruel gaze softened and a tender smile formed on her lips.

"You are young and full of life," she whispered. "Youth is a wonderful thing. I shall let you live.

　雪女は、巳之吉の目をじっと
見つめて、こういいました。
　「でも、もしも、今夜のこと
をだれかに話したら、そのとき
は、そなたのうつくしいいのち
は終わってしまいましょう。」
　そういうと、雪女はまいさわ
ぐ雪の中にすいこまれるよう
に、しずかに立ち去っていきました。
　いま見たことは、ゆめだったのでしょうか――。巳
之吉は、そのまま気を失ってしまったのでした。
　やがて朝になり、気がついた巳之吉は、父の茂作が
こごえ死んでいるのを見つけたのです。
　雪の中で、茂作のとむらいが村人たちの手でおこな
われましたが、巳之吉は、あのふしぎなうつくしい女
のことは、だれにも話しませんでした。
　それから一年の月日がたちました。
　ある雨の日、巳之吉の家のまえに、一人の女が立っ
ておりました。
　「雨でこまってお
いでじゃろう。」
　気だてのいい
巳之吉は、女の
人を家に入れて
やりました。

But remember: if you ever tell anyone about tonight, you too shall die."

Another gust of wind and snow swirled around the room, and the woman was gone. Minokichi's knees buckled, and he fell to the floor unconscious.

Had it been some terrible dream? Perhaps. But Minokichi awoke in the morning to find the door open, the fire out, and his father lying next to him, frozen to death.

Most of the people in the village came to Mosaku's funeral to pay their respects and to comfort Minokichi. "It was the worst blizzard I've ever seen," Minokichi told them, shaking his head sadly and wiping the tears from his eyes. But he told no one about the mysterious woman in white.

A year passed, and another winter came and went. One dark and rainy spring day, Minokichi looked out his window and noticed a young lady sheltering beneath the eaves of his house. Seeing she had no umbrella, he invited her to wait inside until the rain stopped.

女の人は、お雪さんという名でした。身よりもなく、一人で都へでるとちゅうだというのです。すっかり同情した巳之吉は、やさしくその女の人を見つめました。

　二人は、どちらからともなく心をよせあいました。こうして、巳之吉とお雪は夫婦になり、何年もしあわせな月日が流れていきました。

　かわいい子どもにもめぐまれた二人は、それはそれはしあわせでした。

　けれど、ちょっと気がかりなのは、暑い日ざしをうけると、お雪がふらふらとたおれてしまうことです。でも、やさしい巳之吉は、そんなお雪をしっかりとたすけて、暮らしているのでした。

　うつくしい妻、元気な子どもたち。巳之吉はほんとうにしあわせでした。

　そんなある日、針しごとをしているお雪の横顔を見て、ふっと、遠い日のことをおもいだしたのです。

　「のう、お雪。おまえはここにきたときと、すこしもかわらん。

The young lady's name, Minokichi learned, was Yuki. She told him she was on her way to the capital. When he found out she was traveling alone, Minokichi offered to help her in any way he could. They drank tea and talked on and on. And almost before either of them realized it, they had fallen deeply in love.

Yuki never did get to the capital. She stayed with Minokichi, and they were married soon after. It seemed a match made in heaven. As time went by they were blessed with five healthy, handsome children. Yuki was a cheerful, devoted wife and mother, and Minokichi was happier than he had ever been in his life. The only thing that ever really worried him was his wife's delicate health. On hot summer days, Yuki would grow weak and listless. But Minokichi always cared for her lovingly, and the cool breezes of evening never failed to revive her.

One night, as Yuki was doing her sewing, Minokichi looked at her and thought for the thousandth time how lovely she was. "Yuki," he said, "you haven't changed at all. You seem as young and beautiful as the day we met." Gazing at her profile, he suddenly remembered something

いつまでも若くてうつくしい……。だがな、わしは以前に一度だけ、おまえのようにうつくしいおなごを見たことがある。そうじゃ、おまえとそっくりじゃった。」

巳之吉のまぶたには、あのふぶきの夜のことがうかんできました。

お雪が、針しごとの手をとめてたずねます。

「どういう人ですの、その人は……。」

「うん、わしが二十歳のころじゃった。山でふぶいての。そのときじゃ、そのおなごにあったのは。うん、たしかにあれは、雪女……、……じゃった。」

ここまでいったときでした。

「あなた……、とうとう話してしまったのね。あれほどやくそくしていたのに。」

お雪が悲しそうにいいました。

「どうしたんだ、お雪！」

お雪がすくっと立ちあがりました。お雪の着物が、いつのまにか白くかわっています。

「じゃ、おまえは……。」

そうです。お雪こそ、あのときの雪女でした。あの

that had happened long ago. Something he'd never told anyone about. "You know, I just realized," he said, "you remind me a lot of someone I once saw. Or thought I saw."

"Oh? Who was she?" asked Yuki, looking up from her sewing.

"Well, I told you about the blizzard my father and I were caught in when I was twenty. That's when I saw her. I'm still not sure it wasn't just a dream, but..." Minokichi hesitated. "Have you ever heard those stories about the Snow Woman?"

"You had to say it, didn't you?" Yuki's voice was a harsh whisper, and there was a funny look in her eyes. "And you promised. You promised you wouldn't tell anyone."

"What do you mean? Yuki, what's the matter? Where are you going?"

Yuki had stood up and was walking toward the door. And as she moved, her kimono began turning white. White as snow...

"Yuki," Minokichi gasped. "Yuki, you... you're..."

Yes. Yuki was the legendary Snow Woman. And now that Minokichi had broken his promise, she had no choice: she must either leave or destroy him. Fortunately, not even the Snow Woman

夜のことを話されたからには、お雪はもう、人間でいることはできないのです。

「いかないでくれーっ。」

巳之吉がおいすがります。

「どうして、どうしてあなたはしゃべってしまったの。わたしはあなたといつまでも暮らしたかったのよ。」

お雪の目には、なみだがうかんでいます。

「あなたのことは、いつまでもわすれないわ。あなたと暮らしたしあわせな毎日のことも、けっしてわすれないわ。あなたも元気でいてくださいね。

いつまでも、いつまでも――。」

そのとき、戸がばたんと開いて、外からつめたい風がふきこんできました。

そして、お雪のすがたは消えたのです。

巳之吉はあわてて戸口にでてみましたが、もう、お雪のすがたはどこにもありませんでした。

「お雪！　おゆきーっ。」

北国の冬の山には、いまも雪女がいると人はいいます。そして、そのつめたいからだを、あたたかくぬくめてくれる、やさしい人間の心をもとめて、ひゅう、ひゅうと悲しくないて雪の山はだをかけめぐっているということです。

（おわり）

could bring herself to kill the only man she had ever loved.

"Yuki! Don't go!" cried Minokichi, running after her.

"Why, Minokichi? Why did you say it? I wanted to stay with you. I wanted to be your wife forever…" Yuki's cold, dark eyes filled with tears. "I'll never forget you, Minokichi. I'll never forget the happiness I've known with you. Take good care of yourself, and the children… Goodbye, my love."

The door flew open and a cold wind rushed through the room. Then there was silence, and Yuki had vanished. Minokichi ran out the door to the empty street.

"Yuki! Yuki-i-i!"

Minokichi was never to see his wife again. But people in the north country say that on cold, snowy nights, the one they call Yuki Onna—the Snow Woman—still wanders the mountainsides, crying out in a chilling whine. She's searching, they say, for a man who will keep her secret safe and her cold heart warm.

舌切り雀

むかしむかし、あるところに、おじいさんとおばあさんが住んでいましたとさ。

おじいさんは、今日も山で仕事。

「おばあさんや、行ってきますよ。」

おばあさんは、とてもよくばりで、おじいさんがもっと働けばいいと思っていましたから、ぷうんとした顔でおじいさんを見送りました。

でも、おじいさんは、そんなこと、すこしも気にかけていません。おじいさんは、青々とすみきった山の中で働くのが楽しいのです。

「よいしょ。汗を流すのは気分のええこった。どれ、もうひとふんばり。」

The Sparrow's Tongue

There was once an old man who lived with his wife in a little house way out in the country. He was a gentle and honest man whose only joy was to spend his days working in the fields and forest, surrounded by the sights and sounds and smells of nature. His wife, on the other hand, was a greedy and ill-tempered old woman who loved only money. No matter how hard her husband toiled, she was always nagging him to do more.

One morning the old man set out for work as usual. "Well, dear," he said to his wife, "I'm off."

"Try to get something done today, will you?" the old woman said with a scowl. "Time is money, you know."

"Yes, dear." The old man smiled and headed

木を切り、土をほりおこし、畑をつくる仕事です。

「やれやれ、それじゃ、こんどはしばをかるか。」

おじいさんはそういうと、もっと山の奥へ入っていきました。

きれいな森、ひんやりした空気。谷川の音にまじって、小鳥のさえずりも聞こえます。

そんな中で、のんびり働いているおじいさんはとてもしあわせでした。

そのとき、小鳥のなきさけぶような声が聞こえてきました。

「はて、たしかこっちのほうで聞こえたようじゃが……。」

音がしたほうへ目を向けると、

「うっ、ややや……。」

おじいさんは、かれ枝の下でもがいている子すずめをみつけました。

「おお、かわいそうに、けがをしとるな。よしよし……。」

すずめを両手でだきあげて、やさしく話しかけました。

「すぐになおしてやるからな。さ、わしの家にいこう。すぐによくなるよ。」

そういって、子すずめをだいじにふところに入れてやりました。

off to a small plot of land he was clearing. He worked throughout the morning pulling weeds and tilling the soil there, and when he was finished he decided to go a little further up the mountain to gather firewood.

The trees grew thicker here, the leaves were a darker shade of green, and the air was cool and fresh. The old man walked along humming to himself as he picked up fallen twigs, and he was just getting ready to turn back when he heard a tiny voice cry out.

"Help! Tweet, tweet. Oh, help me, pwease!"

The old man followed the sound until he saw where it was coming from. A baby sparrow lay on the ground, trapped by a fallen branch.

"Oh, you poor little thing!" said the gentle old man. He freed the bird and picked it up in the palm of his hand. "You're hurt, aren't you? Come along with me. We'll have you fixed up in no time."

So saying, he carefully placed the sparrow in his waistcoat pocket and headed home.

おじいさんは、家に帰ると、さっそく子すずめのきずの手当てをしました。

　ところが、おばあさんは気にいりません。

　「ふん、仕事はほったらかして、子すずめなんかと遊んでおって……。」

　おばあさんの姿を見て、子すずめはふるえています。

　「まあまあ、ばあさんや、そんなにがみがみいわんでも。このすずめは、けがをしておるんじゃよ。おお、よしよし。」

　おじいさんは、てのひらにのせた米粒をすずめに食べさせました。

　「だいじな米をすずめなんかに食わして、あきれたもんだよ！」

　おばあさんは、すずめをにらみつけてでていきました。

　心のやさしいおじいさんは、子すずめをほうっておく気にはなれません。

　おじいさんは、せっせとこのすずめをかいほうし、おちょんという名まえまでつけてやりました。

　おかげでおちょんは、

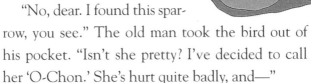

"You're back early," his wife snapped when he walked in the door. "Don't tell me you're tired already?"

"No, dear. I found this sparrow, you see." The old man took the bird out of his pocket. "Isn't she pretty? I've decided to call her 'O-Chon.' She's hurt quite badly, and—"

"Are you losing your mind?" cried the old woman. "Playing with a dirty little bird when there's work to be done!"

"But, dear, I couldn't just leave her to die."

"Why not? What has that stupid sparrow ever done for you? Oh, what's the use? Suit yourself, you old fool. I've got work to do."

The old woman stormed out of the room, leaving her husband alone with the sparrow, who was trembling now with fear.

"There, there, little one," whispered the old man. "Don't mind her. I won't let anyone hurt you."

He tended to the sparrow's wound and was feeding her a few grains of rice when his wife came back into the room.

"What are you doing?" shouted the greedy woman. "Wasting our precious rice on that horrid

元気になっていきました。
　そんなある日、おじい
さんはまた山へでかけて
いきました。
　「おちょんをたのみます
よ、ばあさん。」
　「わかってますよ。」
　おじいさんを見送ると、
おばあさんは、「なにがお
ちょんだ。」とつめたい顔。
こんなふうでしたから、
もちろんえさなどあたえ
るはずもありません。
　おちょんをのこして、さっさと川へ洗濯にいってし
まいました。

little creature! Do you think money grows on trees?"

"Now, dear," said the old man. "Don't get excited. We've plenty to spare, and O-Chon doesn't eat much. Do you, O-Chon?"

"Now you're talking to the foul thing. Have you gone mad?"

The man was so accustomed to his wife's nagging complaints that he merely shrugged and smiled and continued to feed O-Chon.

Thanks to his kindness, the sparrow got better with each passing day. Soon she was hopping about the house and chirping happily, much to the old woman's disgust.

One day the old man left for work especially early. Since he didn't have time to feed O-Chon before he left, he asked his wife to take care of her.

"I'll take care of her, all right," the old woman snapped. But after her husband had gone, she cursed and said, "O-Chon this, O-Chon that. Why did I ever marry such a foolish man?" And later that morning, when she went to the river to wash her clothes, she didn't leave so much as a grain of rice for the sparrow to eat. Hopping about the house, however, O-Chon discovered a bowl of

　ひとりぼっちのおちょんは、おなかがすいて、おばあさんが作ったのりを思わずちゅんちゅん食べはじめました。

　「おいちい、おいちい。」

　とうとうおちょんは、すっかりのりをたいらげてしまいました。

　さあ、たいへん。帰ってきたおばあさんは、かっかとおこりました。

　「まてえ、のりどろぼう。もう二どとできないように、おまえのしたを、こうしてやるう。」

　ちょきーん。

　かわいそうに、おちょんはしたをはさみで切られてしまいました。

　したを切られた子すずめは、なきなき山へ帰っていきました。

starch the old woman had prepared. She jumped up onto the brim of the bowl and had a taste.

"Tweet, tweet. Dee-wishus!"

O-Chon was very hungry, and in no time at all she'd cleaned out the entire bowl. When the old woman came back from the river to starch her clothes, she took one look at the empty bowl, then turned to O-Chon. "Come here, sparrow," she said.

O-Chon saw the angry look in the old woman's eyes and tried to fly away, but the old woman caught her.

"You must be very hungry," she said, baring her teeth in an evil grin. "Open your mouth."

"Tweet."

When she saw the starch on O-Chon's tongue, the old woman reached for her scissors. "Now close your eyes," she hissed.

"Tweet, twee—"

Snip!

O-Chon tried to cry out in pain, only to discover that she couldn't make a sound.

"That's what you get for taking what doesn't belong to you!" the old woman shrieked. "Now get out of here. Out! Out! Out!"

「えっ、なんじゃと、おちょんのしたを！」

話を聞いて、おじいさんは涙を流しました。

「ゆるしておくれ、痛かったろうに。」

おじいさんは、おちょんのことが心配でなりません。おちょんをたずねて、山の奥へと入っていきました。

「おちょんは、どこにいるんじゃろ。」

おじいさんは、林の中をさんざさがしまわりましたが、おちょんの姿はどこにもみえません。

「うむ、そうじゃ。すずめのお宿というのがあるというのを聞いたことがある。そこへ行けば、きっとあのおちょんにあえるにちがいない。」

おじいさんは、もっともっと奥へ入っていきました。

「ちちち、ちちち、こっち、こっち。」

おじいさんの目の前を、二、三羽のすずめが飛びかいました。

The old woman stood at the window screaming and shaking her fist long after O-Chon had disappeared into the forest. In her fist she still held the scissors. In her other hand was the sparrow's tongue.

When the old man came home that evening, his wife calmly told him what she'd done.

"Oh, wife, how could you?" he gasped, his eyes filling up with tears. "How could you be so cruel? Poor, poor O-Chon!"

The old man didn't get a wink of sleep that night, thinking of the pain O-Chon must be in. And when dawn finally came, he leaped up and hurried outside to look for her.

"O-Chon, O-Chon!
Where has she gone?
Who's seen the sparrow
who's lost her tongue?"

The old man had walked for hours, singing these words in a mournful voice, when a group of birds suddenly appeared from out of the trees.

"Tweet, tweet. Tweet, tweet."

　「おお、すずめじゃ。すずめのお宿はどこかの。」

　「こっち、こっち、ちちちち……。」

　おじいさんは、すずめの声にさそわれるように、竹やぶのそのまた奥へ、ずんずん歩いていきました。

　「いらっちゃいませ。ちゅーんとお待ちしておりました。」

　「ところで、おちょんは、どこかい？」

　「ちゅんちゅん、おちょんはこっち。」

　奥のざしきへ入ると、おちょんがかけよってきました。

　「おお、おちょん。おまえのことが心配で、心配で……。」

"Sparrows!" the old man cried. "Do you know of one who's lost her tongue? Do you happen to know where O-Chon has gone?"

"This way. Tweet, tweet. This way, this way!"

Running as fast as his legs would carry him, the old man followed the sparrows, who flew ever deeper into the woods. At last they came to a little bamboo grove. And amid the clumps of bamboo stood a small wooden building. A sign over the gate said "Sparrow's Inn."

"Hewwo, Gwandpa. Welcome!"

The old man rubbed his eyes. The sparrow who had just spoken to him was as big as a person and wore a beautiful silk kimono!

"Pwease come this way. O-Chon is waiting for you."

The astonished old man was led to a room inside, and there he found O-Chon chatting gaily with a flock of friends. All were dressed in silks, and even O-Chon was as big as a young girl.

"O-Chon!"

"Gwandpa!"

"Are you all right?"

"Oh, yes. Tweet, tweet. I'm fine, Gwandpa. My tongue grew back!"

　こうしておじいさんは、おちょんやほかのすずめた
ちの大かんげいをうけました。

　たくさんのごちそうや、楽しい歌やおどりで、おじ
いさんは、すっかり時がたつのを忘れてしまいました。

　でも、いよいよ家へ帰るときがきました。このとき、
すずめたちが、二つのつづらをおじいさんの前へおき
ました。

　「わたしたちのお礼です。大きいほうと小さいほうと、
好きなほうをお持ちになってください。」

　「すまんのう。じゃ、わしは年よりだから、小さいほ
うをもらっていこう。」

54

The old man was so overjoyed to find O-Chon alive and well that he scarcely stopped to wonder at what was happening. The enchanted inn, the kimono-clad sparrows, O-Chon's recovery—miraculous as everything was, somehow it all seemed perfectly natural.

The sparrows decided to have a party to welcome the old man. While he talked happily with O-Chon, they brought out platter after platter of delicious food and saké, and soon they were all laughing and singing and dancing. The old man had such a wonderful time that he stayed until late in the evening. When at last he said he'd have to be going, the sparrows asked him to wait a moment longer.

"We want to give you a pwesent," they said, "for being so kind to O-Chon."

The sparrows brought out two boxes. "Pwease choose one," said O-Chon.

"Well, I'm not as young as I used to be, and it's a long way home. I'd better take the smaller one."

The sparrows helped the old man lift the box onto his back, and they all walked to the gate of the inn to see him off.

"Goodbye, Gwandpa."

　よくのないおじいさんは、小さいつづらを背負って帰っていきました。

　さて、家へ帰ってつづらをあけてみると、でるわでるわ、小判に着物。たくさんの宝物。

　「大きいつづらと小さいつづらをだされたんじゃが、重いのは困るから、小さいほうにしたんじゃ。」

と、おじいさんがいうのを聞いて、おばあさんはおこりました。

　「どこまでまぬけじゃ。大きいほうなら宝物も多かろうに。よしっ、わしが行って、大きいほうをもらってくる。」

　さあ、おばあさんは走りました。山でも坂でもなんのその。欲のかたまりのようになって、つっ走りました。

　すずめのお宿をたずねあてたおばあさんは、わざとらしく笑いながらいいました。

"Goodbye, O-Chon. And thank you for every-thing. I've had a wonderful time. Goodbye, every-one!"

"Goodbye! Tweet, tweet. Goodbye!"

When the old man got home he told his wife all about the Sparrow's Inn and what had hap-pened to him there.

"So this is the present they gave you, is it?" said the old woman. "Let's see what's inside." She lifted the lid and gasped. "We're rich! Rich!"

Inside the box were gold bars, beautiful silks, and jewels of every description.

"Well, how do you like that?" said the old man, chuckling. "You know, they offered me my choice of two boxes, a large one and a small one. The big box looked too heavy, so I—"

"You idiot!" the old woman screamed. "Just think of the treasures there must be in the big one. Where did you say this Sparrow's Inn was?"

As soon as the old man had given her direc-tions, the old woman ran out the door and up the mountain path, determined to get the big present for herself.

When she got to the inn, she asked to see O-Chon.

「おちょんや、わしは
おまえのめんどうをみて
やったはずだね。さあさ
あ、お茶なんかいいから、
早くつづらをおだしよ。」

すずめたちは、二つのつづらをもってきて、おばあ
さんの前におきました。

「わしゃ、この大きいほうさ。足腰はしっかりしてい
るからね。」

「おばあさん、そのつづらは、家へつくまであけない
ようにね。おねがいよ。」

おばあさんは、そんなことに耳もかさず、わが家め
がけて大いそぎ。

でも、よくばりばあさんは、とても家まで待ちきれ
ません。山道のとちゅうで、つづらをおろし、ぎいっ
と、ふたをあけてしまいました。

「あわっ、きゃあ～～～っ。」

つづらの中から煙が上がり、中から出てきたのは化
け物ばかり。一つ目、からかさ、妖怪変化。

おどろいたのなんのって、おばあさんは、ころげる
ようににげだしました。あんまり欲をかきすぎると、

こんなお化けをもらっ
ちゃうぞーっていうお
話は、これでおしまい。

　　　（おわり）

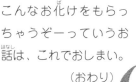

"O-Chon," she said, putting on a phoney smile, "I looked after you when you were hurt, didn't I? All right, then, never mind the tea and cakes. Bring out the boxes."

A large box and a small box were brought and placed before the old woman.

"I'll take the big one," she said. "My legs and back are as strong as any youngster's."

"OK, Gwandma. But pwease don't open it till you get home!"

The old woman paid no attention to O-Chon now. She lifted the box onto her back and, without even saying goodbye, staggered down the path toward home. The box was even heavier than she'd expected, however, and soon she stopped to rest.

"I can't wait to see what's inside," she thought. "I'll just take a little peek before I go on."

She lifted the lid, and what do you think she found?

Gargoyles, goblins, monsters, demons, and fiendish creatures of every description!

Frightened out of her wits, the old woman ran down the mountain screaming at the top of her lungs. And that's how she finally learned that it doesn't pay to be greedy.

しょじょ寺の
狸ばやし

　むかしむかし、山にかこまれた、しょじょ寺という小さなお寺がありました。

　山にはたぬきがいっぱいいて、夜になると寺へやってきては、腹つづみを打ったり、あばれまわったりのいたずらのしほうだいでした。

　おかげで、この寺にはおしょうがいつかず、寺はあれほうだい。

　そのころ、一人の身分の高いおしょうさんが、この寺の話を聞いて、

　「よろしい、わしが行って進ぜよう。」

と、しょじょ寺へやってきました。

The Tanuki Band of Shojoji

The little temple of Shojoji had fallen on hard times. It was surrounded by mountains, the mountains were covered with forests, and the forests were full of the badgers which are known in Japan as tanukis. At night the tanukis would come down to the temple and run wild, causing all sorts of mischief. They especially loved to dance in the garden, beating on their tummies like drums. Thanks to these tanukis, no priest would stay long at Shojoji, and with no one to take care of it, the temple was falling apart.

One day a famous priest heard about what had happened to Shojoji and said, "What a shame. I'll have to go down there and straighten things out."

When he got to the temple after a long journey, the priest was astounded by how run-down it

「うーん、聞きしにまさる
ひどさじゃ。」

おしょうさんは、あまりに
もひどい寺のあれように、あ
きれ顔。

「なんまいだ〜〜〜、なん
まいだあ〜〜〜。」

本堂からひさしぶりにお経
の声が聞こえてきたので、裏
山のたぬきたちは顔をみあわせて、にやり。

さて、そうなるとたぬきたちは、さっそく新しいお
しょうさんを追いだす相談です。

たぬきの親分を中心にひそひ
そ話。

「おい、ぽん太とぽん子、いつ
ものやつ、やってみろ！」

「へ〜〜〜い」

どろどろ、どろ〜〜〜んのぱっ。

ぽん太とぽん子は、なにやら
すがたをかえてしまいました。

「おう、みごとじゃ。早う行っ
ておどかしてこい。」

「なんまいだ〜〜〜、なんまいだあ。」

お経をあげるおしょうさんのうしろにそうっと近づ
いたぽん太は、ぬっと顔を出しました。

was. "It's even worse than they said," he thought as he settled in.

That night, the tanukis in the forest heard the priest chanting his prayers inside the temple. "Mumbo-jumbo, mumble, grumble. Mumbo-jumbo, mumble, grumble..." How long it had been since they'd heard that sound! It was like music to the tanukis' ears, since they loved nothing more than to drive priests crazy. They looked at each other and grinned.

The leader of the tanukis called everyone together to discuss how they would run the new priest out of the temple. "You there, Ponta and Ponko," he said. "Give him the regular treatment."

"Yes, sir!" Ponta and Ponko began spinning around and around, and in a thrice they had changed into something completely different, as tanukis sometimes do.

"Good show!" said the leader. "Now go and scare the living daylights out of him."

Back at the temple, "Mumble, grumble, mumbo-jumbo-o-o." Just as the priest finished, Ponta snuck up from behind and tapped him on the shoulder. The old priest turned around to see a

「ぎゃーっ、あわ
わ……。」
　目のまえにあら
われたのは、一つ
目こぞう。そこへ、
美しいむすめがあ
らわれて、

「おしょうさん、お茶をどうぞ……。」
といいながら、首がにょろにょろっとのびてきたでは
ありませんか。
　「た、た、た、たすけてーっ。」
　おしょうさんは、寺の石段をころげるようにかけお
りて、にげだしてしまいました。
　寺の庭に集まったたぬきたちは、大笑いしながら、
とくいになって腹つづみを打ちつづけておりました。
　さて──、そのつぎにあらわれたのは、とても力の
強そうなごうけつおしょうでした。

　おしょうが寺につ
くと、さっそくたぬ
きたちはおどかしに
かかりました。
　ところが──、
　一つ目こぞうにば
けたぽん太は、頭を
こつんとなぐられ、

little cyclops staring at him with one big eye.

"Aaaiiieee!" screamed the priest. But before he had a chance to recover, a beautiful young lady walked into the room. (It was really Ponko the tanuki, of course.)

"Good evening, Father," she said. "Would you like some tea?" She held out a teapot and smiled, and as she did so her neck began to stretch and stretch until it was as long and squirmy as a giant snake.

"Help!" cried the priest. He ran out to the temple gate, stumbling over the stone steps, and down the road as fast as his legs could carry him.

The rest of the tanukis, who had gathered in the temple garden to watch, split their sides laughing. One by one they began to dance and pound on their tummies, having the time of their lives. They'd succeeded in driving another priest from Shojoji.

Now the next priest who dared to come to the temple was big and strong and mean. No sooner had he arrived than the tanukis were up to their old tricks, but this time things were different. When Ponta showed up in the temple after changing into a baby cyclops, the priest punched

むすめにばけたぽん子が首をにょろにょろのぼすと、首をねじられるしまつ。

「うえーん、いたいよう。」

二ひきは泣き泣き帰ってきました。

たぬきの親分は考えこんでしまいました。

「うーん、あのおしょう、なにに化けてもこわがらん。そうだ、これだ！　一晩じゅう腹つづみを打ちつづけるんだ。そうすればおしょうのやつ、ねむれなくなってまいってしまうぞ。」

てなわけで、その夜もふけて、たぬきたちはいっせいに腹つづみを打ちはじめました。

ぐっすりねむっていたおしょう、さすがにその音で目をさましました。むっくり起き上がり、戸を開けると、

「こらっ、庭で遊んじゃいかーん！」

たぬきたちは、すばやくにげだして、木のかげにかくれてしまいました。

「こら、待てっ。こら、にげるな。たぬきたちのやつ、ばかにしやがって。」

おしょうは庭じゅうたぬきを追いかけまわしましたが、たぬきたちのすばやさには、とてもかないません。

そのうち、石につまずき、石どうろうにぶつかり、

him in the nose. When Ponko arrived in the shape of a young woman and started stretching her neck, the priest tied it in a knot.

"Ow! Ouch! Wa-a-ah!" cried Ponta and Ponko, running back to the forest.

The leader of the tanukis thought things over. "Hmm. We can't scare this priest by changing into spooks, I guess. Let's see… I've got it! We'll drum on our tummies all night long. Then the priest won't be able to get any sleep and he'll have to leave."

So later that night…

Pom pitty pom, pitty pom-pom-pom.

The priest had been fast asleep, but the loud drumming woke him. He got up and went to the door. "Hey!" he shouted. "No playing in the garden!"

The tanukis scampered away, laughing, to hide in the shadows of the trees.

"Stop! Come back out in the open, you little devils! You can't make a fool of me and get away with it!" The priest began chasing the tanukis around the garden, but they were much too fast for him. Finally he tripped on a rock and fell against a stone lantern, bumping his head so

石が頭に落ちて、目をまわしてしまいました。

こうして、おしょうはまたまたたぬきたちにやられてしまったのです。

さてさて、そのつぎにあらわれたのは、なんともきたないおしょうさん。このおしょうさんは、きたない寺がすっかり気に入ったとみえて、いついてしまいました。

たぬきたちは、さっそくおしょうさんを追いだす相談です。

まず、一つ目こぞうのぽん太があらわれましたが——。

「おう、これはかわいい一つ目こぞうじゃあ。どら、だんごでも食わんか。」

ぽん太はおしょうさんにだんごをもらって、とことこ帰ってきました。

こんどは、ぽん子ねえさんです。ところが、おしょうさんは大よろこび。

「おう、みごとみごと。さあ、一ぱいいこう。」

と、ぽん子にお酒を飲ませるしまつ。

たぬきの親分はおこりました。

「ようし、こうなったらあの手だ！」

68

hard that all he could see for the rest of the night was stars.

The following day, the big, strong priest packed his bags and left Shojoji, never to return. Chalk up another victory for the tanukis. But their luck was about to change.

Next to arrive was a very shabby-looking priest dressed in old rags. He liked the dirty, run-down temple as soon as he saw it, and decided to stay. The tanukis, of course, held another meeting, and Ponta turned himself into a cyclops again. But when he went to the temple...

"Oh! What a cute little cyclops," said the shabby priest. "Here, have one of these rice dumplings."

Ponta was bewildered. He accepted a dumpling and trotted back to the forest. Now it was Ponko's turn. But when she came and stretched her neck, the priest only laughed and clapped his hands.

"That's great!" he said. "How did you do that? Here, let's have a drink." The priest poured out a glass of rice wine for Ponko.

The tanuki leader was shocked when he heard how Ponta and Ponko had been treated. "If that's the way it is," he said, "There's only one thing left to do."

というわけで、その夜、おしょうさんが寝ころんだころ……。

　物音で目をさましたおしょうさんが戸を開けると、たぬきたちが勢ぞろいで腹つづみを打っています。

「わあっ、こりゃおもしろい。わしも仲間に入れてくれ！」

　ずいぶんかわったおしょうさんです。たぬきたちの仲間に入り、いっしょに腹つづみを打ちはじめました。

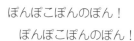

ぽんぽこぽんのぽん！

　ぽんぽこぽんのぽん！

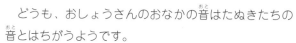

　どうも、おしょうさんのおなかの音はたぬきたちの音とはちがうようです。

「わーい、なんだ、なんだ、その音は。わっはっは、はっはっは。」

　たぬきたちに笑われて、おしょうさんは、もういっしょうけんめい。

「よせよせ、腹がこわれてしまうぞ。」

　たぬきの親分がとめるのも聞かず、おしょうさんはたたきつづけます。

　そのうち、おなかをたたきすぎたおしょうさん、とうとうふらふらになってたおれてしまいました。

That night, no sooner had the priest fallen asleep than he was awakened by a great hubbub in the garden. He got up, went to the door, and looked out to see dozens of tanukis thumping their bellies.

"Gee," said the priest, "that looks like fun! May I join you?" He ran outside and began pounding his stomach along with all the astonished tanukis. They had never run into a priest like this before.

Pock picky pock, picky pock-pock-pock.

The sound the priest's stomach made seemed strange to the tanukis. They thought it was very funny. "Hee, hee, hee! Listen to that!"

When he realized the tanukis were laughing at him, the priest only tried all the harder.

"That's enough," the tanuki leader finally told him. "You'd better rest awhile, before your tummy explodes." But the priest wouldn't hear of it. He kept trying to get a better sound. Before long he began to stagger and soon he collapsed on the ground.

「そーれ、いわんこっちゃない。このままじゃ、かぜをひいてしまうぞ。おしょうさんを寺の中へ運んでやれ。」

おしょうさんを追いだそうとしたたぬきたちでしたが、おしょう

さんをしんせつにかいほうしました。

つぎの日の朝。

「はて、わしはいつここへもどったんじゃろう。ゆんべは腹つづみを打って……。まあ、それはどうでもいい。もうすこし腹つづみがうまくならんといかんな。」

というわけで、おしょうさんは朝早くから腹つづみの練習をはじめました。

「強くたたけばいいってもんじゃねえべ。こつじゃよ、こつ。そいつをおぼえねば……。」

熱心なおしょうさんは、昼めしもそこそこに、またも腹つづみのけいこです。

やがて、おてんとさまが西にかたむくころ、おしょうさんのおなかの音は、かなりいい音が出るようになっていました。

さて、今夜は満月です。

おしょうさんもたぬきたちも、早くから寺の庭に勢ぞろいして、みんなで楽しく腹つづみです。

"See? Didn't I tell him?" said the leader. "We'd better carry him into the temple before he catches his death of cold." So the tanukis, who had intended to drive the priest away, ended up looking after him. Then man's simple, friendly nature had won them over.

The next morning, the priest woke up and said, "Funny… I don't remember coming back to bed last night. Let's see… I was out in the garden pounding on my belly… Oh, well, that's neither here nor there. The main thing is to improve my tummy-thumping." The priest lost no time in starting to practice. "It's not just a question of how hard you hit your stomach. There's a certain knack to it. Maybe if I cup my hands…"

He practiced all morning. Then he ate a quick lunch and went right back to his training. What determination!

That night, the shabby-looking priest joined the tanukis in the garden again. They had a wonderful time, drumming away for all they were worth in the light of the full moon.

ぽんぽこぽん、ぽんぽこぽん。

ぽんぽこぽんの、すっぽっぽん。

おしょうさんのおなかの音がずいぶんよくなったの

で、たぬきたちも負けては
おられません。

「おしょうさんに負ける
な、負けるな。」

と、ひっしでおなかをたた
いているうちに、たぬきの
親分のおなかはどんどんふ
くれていきました。

それでもたたきつづけます。

ぱーん！

とうとうおなかがはれつして、たぬきの親分はひっ
くりかえってしまいました。

「こりゃたいへんじゃあ！　薬、薬。」

おしょうさんは、あわてて薬を持ってかけつけ、た
ぬきのおなかにぬってやりました。

「どうだ、ぐあいは……。」

心配そうにたずねるおしょうさんに、たぬきの親分
はにっこりしていいました。

「おしょうさんのおかげで、もうなおったよ。さーて、
続きをやるぞうっ。それっ、あいててて……。」

たぬきの親分は、うでをふり上げましたが、まだむ
りなようです。

Pom pitty pom, pitty pom-pom-pom.

The priest was very good now, and the tanukis weren't about to be outdone. "Don't let him show you up!" shouted the leader, who was beating his own stomach so hard that it began to swell up frightfully. In his excitement, however, he scarcely noticed and continued drumming until…

Bam!

The leader's stomach exploded. He fell over backwards and lay there moaning.

"Oh! This is terrible! Medicine! Bring some medicine!"

The shabby priest hurried into the temple and came back with a jar of salve. He rubbed it on the leader's stomach and asked, "How do you feel?"

The tanuki smiled up at him and said, "I'm much better now, thank you. Let's get on with the show! A–one, a–two, a— Ow! Ow! Ow!" He was ready to continue, but his stomach wasn't.

「つぎの満月までしんぼうしなさい。みんな、今夜は親分のおなかが早くなおるよういのって、元気よくやろう。」

「は～～い。」

おしょうさんのかけ声に、たぬきたちが声をそろえてこたえます。

こうして、たぬきたちとゆかいなおしょうさんは、朝まで元気よく腹つづみを打ちつづけました。

そして、しょじょ寺というこの寺では、いまでも満月の夜には、たぬきたちが庭に集まって、腹つづみを打つという話ですよ。

（おわり）

"You'd better take it easy for a month or so," said the priest. "Try to hold out till the next full moon. OK, everybody! Are you ready?"

"YEAH!" shouted all the tanukis.

The leader sat on a rock and watched while the jolly priest and the rest of the tanukis drummed the night away.

And they say that even now the tanukis gather in the garden of Shojoji and drum on their tummies whenever the moon is full.

耳なし芳一

（山口県のお話）

　むかしむかしのこと。いまの下関が赤間とよばれていたころのお話です。

　阿弥陀寺というお寺がありました。そのお寺に、芳一という琵琶弾きがおりました。芳一は、幼いころから目が不自由だったため、琵琶の弾き語りをしこまれ、まだほんの若者ながら、その芸は師匠をしのぐほどになっていました。阿弥陀寺のおしょうさんは、そんな芳一の芸を見こんで、寺にひきとったのでした。

　芳一は、源平の物語を語るのがとくいで、とりわけ、壇の浦の合戦のくだりを語るときには、その真にせまった語りに、だれ一人、なみだをさそわれぬものはなかったそうです。

Earless Ho-ichi

Long ago the town of Shimonoseki was known as Akama. On the outskirts of Akama stood Amida Temple. And in this temple lived a musical monk named Ho-ichi.

Ho-ichi had been blind since birth. As a child, he learned to play a kind of lute called the biwa. He studied and practiced very hard, and now, though still young, he was a great master of the instrument. People came from all over the country to hear Ho-ichi perform the epic tale of the famous Heike clan. They especially loved the way he sang the last part of the tale, about the great Battle of Dannoura.

そのむかし、壇の浦で、源氏と平家の長いあらそいの、最後の決戦がおこなわれ、戦いにやぶれた平家一門は、女や子どもにいたるまで、安徳天皇として知られている幼帝もろとも、ことごとく海にしずんでしまいました。

この、かなしい平家最後の戦いを語ったのが、壇の浦のくだりなのです。

むし暑い夏の夜のこと。

おしょうさんが法事ででかけてしまったので、芳一は、一人お寺にのこって琵琶のけいこをしておりました。

すると、

「芳一！　芳一！」

と、よぶ声がするのです。

「どなたさまでしょう。わたしは目が不自由ですので。」

すると、声の主はこたえます。

「わしは、この近くにおられる、さる身分の高いお方の使いのものじゃ。

殿が、そなたの語りをきいてみたいとお望みじゃ。さっそく館へ案内するによって、ついてまいれ。」

The Battle of Dannoura took place at sea, in the Straits of Shimonoseki. It marked the end of the long, bloody feud between the Heike and Genji clans. The battle ended with the defeat of the Heike, most of whom were killed. And among the victims was the eight-year-old Emperor Antoku. It's a tragic tale indeed, and when Ho-ichi played and sang it, no one could listen without shedding a tear.

One hot, humid summer night, the priest and the other monks of Amida Temple all went off to chant sutras at a funeral in town. Ho-ichi was alone in the temple playing the biwa when he heard someone call his name.

"Ho-ichi! Ho-chi!"

"Who's there? Who is it?"

"I am the messenger of a great lord who lives nearby," answered the voice. "His lordship has learned of your skill with the biwa and wishes to hear you play and sing. Follow me and I'll lead you to the castle."

芳一は、身分の高いお方が自分の琵琶をききたがっているると聞いて、すっかりこうふんしてついていきました。

　使いのものが歩くたび、がしゃがしゃとよろいのすれる音がします。きっと、よろいに身をかためた、りっぱな武者なのでしょう。

　やがて、大きな門を通り、広い庭を通り……、大きな館につきました。

　そこには、おおぜいの人が集まっているらしく、さらさらという絹ずれの音や、よろいのふれ合う音が聞こえていました。

　女官らしき人がいいました。

「芳一、さっそく、平家の物語を語ってくだされ。」

「かしこまりました。」

　芳一は、琵琶を鳴らして語りはじめました。

　舟にあたってくだける波、弓鳴りの音、兵士たちのおたけびの声、息たえて海に落ちる武者たちの音……。それらをたくみにあらわす、芳一の琵琶の音に、大広間はたちまちのうちに、壇の浦の合戦場になってしまったかのようでした。

Ho-ichi was thrilled that such an illustrious person wanted to hear his music. He eagerly followed the messenger, whose armor clanked and rattled. No doubt the messenger himself was a dashing and noble samurai.

At length they passed through a large gate, across a spacious garden, and into an enormous banquet hall. A great crowd of people seemed to be gathered there. Ho-ichi could hear the rustle of silks and the clatter of armor on all sides.

"We've been waiting for you, Ho-ichi," came the gentle voice of a woman. "Please sing the tale of the Heike for us."

"As you wish, your ladyship."

Ho-ichi took a seat and began to sing and pluck at his biwa. Never before had he played with such emotion. When he came to the final battle scene, he sang of the waves crashing over the decks, of the twanging bow strings and the cries and shouts of the doomed warriors. And his biwa echoed

そして、平家のかなしい
最期のくだりになると、広
間のあちこちにむせび泣き
がおこり、芳一の琵琶が終
わってもしばらくは、口を
きく人もなく、しいんと
静まりかえっていました。

　やがて、さっきの女官
がいいました。
　「ごくろうさまでした。
　そなたの琵琶のうでは、
聞きしにまさるもの、殿もたいそうよろこんでおられ
ます。」
　「ありがとうございます。」
　芳一がお礼をいうと、女官はつづけました。
　「殿が、なんぞふさわしいお礼をくださるそうじゃ。
　なれど、今夜より六日間、毎夜そなたの琵琶を聞き
たいとの仰せ。よってあすの夜も、この館にまいられ
るように。それから、寺にもどっても、このことはだ
れにも話してはならぬ。よろしいな。」
　そのつぎの夜も、芳一は、迎えにきた武者にしたが
い、館へ行くと、昨夜と同じように琵琶を弾きました。
　ところが、明け方近く寺にもどった芳一は、おしょ
うさんに見つかってしまったのです。おしょうさんは、
夜どおしどこへ行っていたのかと、たずねましたが、

each sound so faithfully that the listeners felt as if they were reliving that fateful fight. They were all deeply moved. Gradually the hall filled with muffled sobs, and when Ho-ichi had finished, no one spoke for some time.

"Ho-ichi," said the gentlewoman at last, "that was very beautiful. His lordship, also, has asked me to express his appreciation."

"The pleasure and honor are mine," said Ho-ichi, bowing.

"So pleased was his lordship, in fact," the lady went on, "that he wants you to return each night this week to play for us. You will be handsomely rewarded. But you must not mention this to anyone. Is that understood?"

After solemnly giving his word, Ho-ichi took leave of the company and was escorted back to the temple.

The next night the samurai messenger came again to lead Ho-ichi to the castle. Again he played and sang the Heike tale, and again the lords and ladies wept.

This time Ho-ichi didn't get back to the temple till the dawn. The priest saw him returning and asked where he'd been all night, but Ho-ichi

芳一は、館でのやくそくを守って、一言も話しませんでした。

　おしょうさんは、芳一がなにもいわないので、なにか深いわけがあるにちがいないと思い、もし、芳一がでかけるようなことがあれば、あとをつけるように、と、寺男たちにいっておいたのでした。

　寺男たちは、芳一が雨の中、寺を出たので、そっとあとをつけていきました。ところが、目の不自由なはずの芳一の足は意外に早く、闇夜にかき消されるように、すがたが見えなくなってしまったのです。

「いったいどこへ行ったんだ？」

「もう一度、そのあたりをさがしてみよう。」

と、あちこちさがしまわり、寺男たちは墓地へやってきました。

　ぴかっ！　いなびかりに、雨にぬれた墓石がうきあがります。

　そのいなびかりに、寺男たちは、芳一のすがたを見つけたのです。

「あっ！　あそこ！」

「芳一さんだ！」

　寺男たちは、おどろきのあまり立ちすくみました。

　寺男たちの見た光景は、こうでした。

　安徳天皇の墓の前で、ずぶぬれになって琵琶を弾く

remembered his promise and refused to answer. This made the priest suspicious, and he ordered the monks to keep an eye on the blind man.

That night there was a tremendous thunderstorm. Two monks were sitting by an open door, watching the rain pour down, when they spotted Ho-ichi leaving the temple. They immediately set out to follow him as instructed. But blind Ho-ichi moved so quickly through the darkness that he left the two monks far behind.

"Where could he have gone?"

"I don't know. But we've got to find him."

After searching for over an hour in the pouring rain, however, they gave up and headed back to the temple. They were taking a shortcut through the cemetery when a great streak of lightning lit up the sky.

"L-look!" cried one of the monks. "It's Ho-ichi!"

The two men froze with fear at the sight before them. In front of the grave of the Emperor Anotku sat Ho-ichi with

芳一。そして、その芳一のまわりを飛びかう無数の鬼火……。

寺男たちは、芳一が亡霊にとりつかれているにちがいない、と、力まかせに芳一を寺につれもどしました。そのとおり、芳一は亡霊にとりつかれていたのです。無念のなみだをのんで海にしずんでいった平家一族の亡霊に。

そのできごとを聞いたおしょうさんは、魔よけのまじないをして、芳一を亡霊から守ることにしました。

つぎの夜、おしょうさんは、芳一の体じゅうに経文を書くと、いいました。

「芳一、おまえの人なみはずれた芸が亡霊をよぶことになってしまったようじゃ。よく聞けよ、芳一。

今夜もわしは、村のお通夜にでかけるが、だれがきてもけっして口をきいてはならんぞ。亡霊にしたがったものは命をとられる。

しっかり座禅を組んで、身じろぎひとつせぬことじゃ。おそれて返事をしたりすれば、おまえは今度こそころされてしまうじゃろう。わかったな。」

「はい。」

his biwa. And all around him danced dozens of phantom lights! These, the monks realized, were the spirits of the Heike who had perished in the nearby sea so long ago. Little did the blind musician know who he was playing for.

Seeing the danger Ho-ichi was in, the two monks ran to rescue him. With the ghostly lights buzzing around them like angry bees, they grabbed the blind man and dragged him out of the cemetery and back to the temple.

The next day, when the priest heard what had happened, he was beside himself with worry. He summoned Ho-ichi, called for a brush and ink, and proceeded to write Buddhist sutras all over the blind man's body.

When he'd written the last of the holy words, he laid down his brush and said, "Ho-ichi, tonight I must go to town again and I won't be here to help you. These sutras I've written on your body will make you invisible to spirits. But you are in great danger. You must do exactly as I tell you. If anyone should come and speak to you, do not answer them. Sit quietly in meditation and don't move a muscle. Your life depends upon it!"

"Yes, Master."

芳一が座禅を組んでいると、いつものように武者の声がしてきました。

「芳一、芳一！」

しかし、芳一のすがたはありません。経文を書いた芳一の体は、亡霊の目には見えないのです。芳一をさがして、寺の中へ入ってきた武者は、宙にういている二つの耳を見つけました。

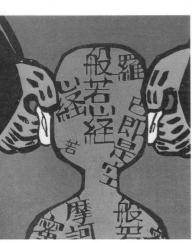

そう、おしょうさんは、耳にだけ、経文を書きわすれてしまったのでした。

亡霊はいいました。

「この耳だけでも持ちかえって、芳一をよびにいった証とせねばなるまい。」

そして、芳一の耳に手をかけると、その耳をもぎとってかえっていったのでした。芳一は、その間もずっと、座禅を組んだまま、身じろぎひとつしませんでした。

夜明けまえ、いそいで寺にもどったおしょうさんは、芳一のいる座敷にかけこみました。

「芳一！　芳一、無事か？」

芳一は、じっと、座禅を組んでいました。しかし、その両の耳はなく、耳のあったところからは、血が流

That night Ho-ichi was meditating alone in the temple when he heard the samurai messenger's voice.

"Ho-ichi... Ho-ichi..."

But the blind man sat perfectly still and made no reply. And all the ghostly messenger could see were two ears floating in the air. That's right. The priest had forgotten to brush the holy words over Ho-ichi's ears!

"I guess he's not here," sighed the ghost. "Looks like he left his ears behind, though. I'd better take these back with me to prove I tried to find him."

The ghost took an ear in each hand and pulled. *Rip!* He peeled them right off Ho-ichi's head! Terrible as the pain was, however, Ho-ichi remembered the priest's warning and didn't move or make a sound.

When the priest returned to the temple in the morning, he hurried to Ho-ichi's room to see if he was all right. And as soon as he saw the blood on the sides of the

れておりました。それを見たおしょうさんには、すべ
てのことがわかりました。

　「そうであったか……。耳に経文を書きわすれるとは。
かわいそうなことをしてしもうたのう。

　いい医者をたのんで、てあつく手あてをしてもらう
としよう。」

　芳一は両の耳をとられてしまいましたが、それから
はもう、亡霊につきまとわれることもなく、医者の手
あてのおかげで傷もよくなりました。

　やがて、この話は、口から口へと伝わり、芳一の琵
琶は、ますます評判になっていきました。そして、芳
一は、いつしか「耳なし芳一」とよばれるようになり、
その名を知らぬ人はいないほど、有名な琵琶法師にな
ったということです。

（おわり）

92

blind man's head, he realized what had happened. "Ah, Ho-ichi," he moaned. "You poor fellow. I forgot to write on your ears!"

But at least Ho-ichi was still alive, and the spirits never came back to bother him. Though he'd lost both ears, he continued to play the biwa and sing. He became more famous than ever, and before long there wasn't a soul in the country who hadn't heard of Earless Ho-ichi, the musical priest.

分福茶釜

（分福—福を分けること。）

（群馬県のお話）

　むかしむかし、あるところに、古道具を集めるのが、なによりの楽しみというおしょうさんがおりましたとさ。

　ある日のこと、おしょうさんは、また、古い茶がまを買いこんでまいりました。

　おしょうさんは、茶がまを自分のへやにおくと、しげしげとながめたり、においをかいだり。

　「くんくん……、ちとくさいのう……。おうい！　だれかおらんか。」

　おしょうさんによばれ、こぼうずたちがやってきました。

　「はい、なんですか、おしょうさん。」

　「すまんが、この茶がまを洗っとくれ。たっぷり砂を

94

Bunbuku Teakettle

Long, long ago, at Morinji Temple in Gunma Prefecture, there lived a certain priest who loved nothing more than collecting curios. One day this priest returned to the temple with an old teakettle he'd bought in town. He went straight to his room and inspected his purchase carefully. He even sniffed at it.

Sniff, sniff. "Hm… Smells a little funny," he said, wrinkling his nose. "Yoo-hoo! Where is everybody?"

Two of the young boys who lived and studied at the temple came running. "Yes, Master?"

"I want you to clean this teakettle for me. Use

つけてみがくんじゃぞ。」

　さて、いいつけられたこぼうずたち、毎度のことなので、洗い方も乱暴です。

　「自分で洗えばいいのに……。」

　文句いいながら洗っていると……。

　「いたい！」

　なんと、茶がまが悲鳴をあげたではありませんか。

　「ひゃあ！」

　「ちゃ、茶がまが口をきいたぞ！」

　こぼうずたちは、もうびっくり。大あわてで、おしょうさんのところにころがりこみました。

　「た、たいへんです。おしょうさん！」

　「ちゃ、茶がまが口をきいたんです。」

　でも、そんな話、おしょうさんが信じるはずありません。

　「おまえたち、洗うのがいやで、いいかげんなこといっとるな。もうよい。洗ったら水を入れてもってきなさい。」

　おしょうさんにそういわれ、こぼうずたちは、水を入れた茶がまをもってくると、それをいろりにかけ、こわごわ後ずさりしました。

　いろりの上の茶がまは、なにごともないかのようにみえます。

plenty of sand, and polish it till it's nice and shiny."

The boys carried the kettle outside, grumbling. "Why doesn't he clean it himself?" they complained. They were slapping handfuls of wet sand on the teakettle and scrubbing away recklessly when something incredible happened: the kettle jumped out of their hands and screamed.

"Ouch! That hurts!"

"Aaaiiieee!" The boys leaped up and ran to the priest, stumbling and falling over each other.

"M-Master! Help!"

"The teakettle... It t-talked!"

The priest, of course, didn't believe them. "You'll do anything to get out of a little work, won't you?" he scolded. "You ought to be ashamed of yourselves, coming to me with a story like that. Enough of this nonsense! Fill the kettle with water and bring it here."

Reluctantly, the boys did as they were told. They rinsed the kettle out carefully, filled it with water, and carried it to the priest's room. The priest set it over the fire, and the boys backed away, trembling with fear.

Sitting on the fire, however, it looked to the

おしょうさんは、こぼうずたちにいいました。

「まったく、いいかげんなことばかりいいおって。わ
しもぜひ聞きたいものじゃ
な。その茶がまがしゃべる
のを。」

と、そのとき、

「あついっ！」
という、悲鳴とともに、と
つぜん、茶がまから勢いよ
く水がふきだしました。

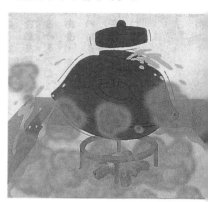

「うひゃあ！」

「な、なんじゃ、これは……。」

いくら古道具ずきのおしょうさんでも、しゃべる茶
がまなんてはじめてのこと、すっかりきみが悪くなっ
てしまいました。

ちょうどそこへ、どうぐやさんが顔をだしました。

「そうじゃ。これをもっていってもらおう。おーい、
どうぐやさん。」

おしょうさんによばれたどうぐやさんは、茶がまを

みて、大よろこび。

「えっ？　ただでくれる
だか？　こんなりっぱな茶
がまをただでもらえると
は、やっとおらにも運がま
わってきただな。」

priest like any old teakettle. "Hmph. Always coming up with ridiculous stories, aren't you?" he said, scowling. "Talking teakettles, indeed! That'll be the day!"

Well, no sooner had he said this than there was a loud cry—"Ow! It's hot!"—and the teakettle began shaking and spurting out water, making a sound like this: *Bun-buku, sssss! Bun-buku, sssss!*

The boys ran screaming out of the room, and it was all the horrified priest could do to keep from running with them. However much he loved curios, he wanted no part of a talking teakettle. It was the spookiest thing he'd ever seen, and he decided to get rid of it as soon as possible.

As luck would have it, a poor tinker was passing by just at that moment.

"I know," thought the priest. "I'll give it to him." He stepped outside and waved. "Hallo-o! Mr. Tinker!"

When the tinker was told he could have the teakettle, he was overjoyed. "You're going to give me this kettle for free?" he said. "Well, how do you like that? My luck must be changing at last." He tucked the teakettle under his arm and headed for home, humming contentedly.

　なんにも知らないどうぐやさん、ほくほく茶がまをかかえて帰ると、夕はんには、尾頭つきのさかなをふんぱつしました。
　「尾頭つきなんて、何年ぶりだべ。いやあ、茶がまさまさまだ。」と、おぜんの前に腰をおろし、いざ食べようとすると……、
　「ありゃ！　さかながねえ！」
　せっかくの尾頭つきがきえています。大あわてで、あっちこっちさがしまわりましたが、影も形もありません。どうぐやさんは、もう、がっくり。
　「そうだよ、そんなもんだよ。りっぱな茶がまをただでもらって、よろこんでりゃ、焼いたさかなはにげていく。ああ、やっぱりおらには、運がねえ。」

　このどうぐやさん、運にめぐまれないうえに、お人よしで、商売がへた。これでは、貧乏からぬけ出せるはずがありません。

　「なにもかも夢……。ねよう。」
　ごろっと、横になった、そのとき、
　「すみません。おさかな食べちゃったのはわたしです。」
　声がしたと思ったら、茶がまに手がはえ、足がはえ……、たぬきのような首としっぽがにゅっと出て、こちらをみているではありませんか！

And that wasn't the end of the tinker's apparent good fortune. Later that evening a friend of his stopped by his house with a most welcome gift: a large, freshly caught fish.

"I haven't eaten a whole fish in years," the tinker thought as he grilled it over the fire. "First the teakettle and now this. What a day!" But when he sat down at the table after washing his hands…

"Oh, no! My fish is gone!" The meal he had so looked forward to eating had vanished. He searched everywhere, but the fish was nowhere to be found. "Isn't that just my luck? I'm about to celebrate getting this nice little teakettle and my dinner disappears. Oh, well. It won't be the first time I've gone to sleep on an empty stomach."

Sighing, the tinker got ready for bed. No sooner did he lay down and close his eyes, however, than a voice in the darkness said, "Forgive me, Mr. Tinker. I'm the one who ate your fish." The startled man sat up and opened his eyes. And guess what he saw. The teakettle was sprouting the head, legs, and tail of a tanuki!

「ちゃ、茶がまがたぬきに
ばけた！」

　あわててにげようとする
どうぐやさんに、茶がまだ
ぬきはいいました。

「おどかして、すみません。かけだしのたぬきです。」

「ああ、おどろいた、たぬきが茶がまにばけてただか。」

「すみません。たいせつなおさかな食べちゃって……。」

「ああ、ええだよ、生きものなら、はらもへるでよ。」

　どうぐやさんのやさしいことばに、
たぬきは、泣きだしました。

「くすん、くすん……。おねが
いです。わたしをここへおいて
ください。」

「なにいうだ。おらはごらんのと
おりの貧乏暮らし、たぬきを飼うゆと
りなどありゃしねえ。山へ帰るがいいだ。」

　するとたぬきは、泣き泣き身の上話を
はじめたのです。

「山にいるとき、仲間とばけく
らべをしたんです。ところが、
わたしだけ、元にもどれなくな
ってしまいました。こんな姿じ
ゃ、はずかしくて、山へ帰るこ
とはできません……。」

102

"It's alive!" shouted the tinker. He was getting ready to run outside when the teakettle spoke to him again.

"I didn't mean to frighten you. I'm really just a plain old tanuki—and not a very clever one, either."

"What? Oh, now I get it. So you're only a tanuki who turned himself into a teakettle. Phew! You did give me quite a scare, you little rascal."

"I'm really sorry about eating that fish."

"Oh, that's all right. Forget it. You must have been hungry."

No one had ever spoken so kindly to the tanuki before. His little eyes filled with tears. "You're such a nice man," he sobbed. "Can I stay here with you?"

"Don't be silly. Look how poor I am. I can't afford to keep you. You'd better go back to the mountains where you belong."

But the tanuki, still sobbing, shook his head and said, "You don't understand. When I was in the mountains, my friends and I had a turning-into-things contest. But I was the only one who couldn't turn back into a proper tanuki. I can't go home like this—I'm too ashamed!"

どうぐやさんは、たぬきに同情して、その夜は、た
ぬきをとめてやりました。

　つぎの日の朝、どうぐやさんが目をさますと、茶が
まだぬきは、しんけんな表情でこういうのです。

　「どうか、わたしをここにおいてください。お金なら、
わたしがかせぎます。」

　「おまえがかせぐって？」

　「はい、芸をするのです。
あなたは見せ物小屋を作っ
てください。」

　さて、よく日、にわか作
りの見せ物小屋で、茶がま
だぬきの芸のはじまり。

　「さあ、らっしゃい、ら
っしゃい。

　その名もおもしろおかし

い、分福茶がまの綱渡りぃ〜〜〜。」

　どうぐやさんのたたくたいこに合わせ、たぬきは、
綱の上でおどります。

　このめずらしい、分福茶がまの綱渡りは、うわさに
うわさをよんで、大人気。つぎからつぎへとお客がや
ってきては、やんややんやと、お金をばらまきます。

　どうぐやさんも、やっと貧乏か
らおさらばして、人並のくらし
ができるようになりました。

"All right, look," said the tinker. "I'll put you up for tonight. But in the morning you'll have to go."

The next day, however, the tanuki pleaded with him again.

"Please let me stay. If it's money you're worried about, I can earn my keep."

"You! How?"

"I can perform tricks. All you have to do, Mr. Tinker, is make a little show tent, and people will pay to watch me."

It seemed like a crazy idea, but the tanuki was very persuasive. Soon the tinker was setting up a tent in the front yard. And the very next day they gave their first public performance.

"Come one, come all. See the tanuki tightrope-walker with the wondrous and amusing name—Bunbuku Teakettle!" The teakettle-tanuki danced on the high wire to the beat of the tinker's drum, and the crowd roared with delight.

Before long, Bunbuku Teakettle's antics on the tightrope had become the talk of the countryside. People came from far and wide to watch his show, and the money poured in. Soon the tinker was living a life of luxury. Of course, he never forgot that he owned it all to his little friend.

そんなある晩のこと。どうぐやさんは、なにやら熱心に本を読んでいます。

「なにしてるんですか。」

「おまえが元の姿にもどれる方法はないかと、思ってな。おまえにはずいぶん世話になったからな。今度は、わしがおまえになにかしてやる番さ。」

それをきいたたぬきは、首を横にふりました。

「いいえ！ わたしは、いまのままでしあわせです。毎日、楽しいんです。」

それから二年がすぎました。どうぐやさんは、たぬきをなんとか元の姿にもどしてやろうと、あれこれ手をつくしましたが、どれもこれもだめでした。

たぬきは、このままでしあわせだと、口ぐせのようにいっていたのですが、やはり、茶がまにばけたままの姿にはむりがあったのでしょう。ある寒い日、とうとう高い熱をだしてたおれてしまったのです。

そんなたぬきを、どうぐやさんは心をこめて看病し

ました。

「なあ、分福、春になって元気になったら、花見にいこうや。にぎりめしもってよ……。」

「おやじさん……。」

One night the tinker was in his room reading a book. Bunbuku came in, sat down beside him, and asked, "What are you doing?"

"I'm trying to find a way to help you turn back into a real tanuki. You've done so much for me, and now I want to do something for you."

The teakettle-tanuki shook his head. "No!" he cried. "I like it the way I am. I'm enjoying myself every day!"

Two years passed. They were the two happiest years of Bunbuku's life. During this time, the tinker continued to try to find some way to free his little friend from the teakettle, but nothing worked. Bunbuku, meanwhile, never tired of repeating that he liked being just the way he was.

Having a kettle for a body would be hard on anyone, though. One very cold winter's day, Bunbuku collapsed with a dangerously high fever.

The tinker tried his best to nurse him back to health and to cheer him up. "Bunbuku," he would say, "in the spring, when you're better, we'll go see the cherry blossoms. Won't that be fun? We'll take some rice cakes with us and we'll sing songs and dance, and…"

The teakettle-tanuki's eyes would fill with

どうぐやさんのあたたかい心につつまれ、たぬきは
いま、ほんとうにしあわせでした。そして、その夜、
分福は、元の姿にもどれないまま、息をひきとってし
まったのです。

「分福！　分福う！」

どうぐやさんが、いくら泣きさけんでも、分福はも

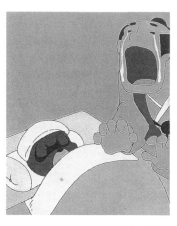

う二度と目をあける
ことはありませんで
した。

なげき悲しんだど
うぐやさんは、茶が
まをだいじにお寺に
運んで、りっぱな供
養をしてもらいまし
た。話をきいたおし
ょうさんは、その茶

がまをゆずりうけ、お寺の宝にしました。

茶がまは、いまでも、茂林寺というお寺にあるとい
うことです。

（おわり）

108

tears of joy as he listened to the tinker's kind words. But he knew it was not to be. One night he called his friend to his bedside and whispered a short, painful goodbye.

"Bunbuku!" cried the tinker. "Please don't die!" But it was too late. The teakettle-tanuki had breathed his last.

In the morning, the tinker sadly carried his lifeless teakettle back to the curio-loving priest. Impressed by Bunbuku's amazing story, the priest promised to keep the kettle as one of Morinji Temple's most valued treasures. And that's where it remains to this day.

赤ん坊になった
おばあさん

むかしむかし、あるところに、じいさまとばあさまが住んでおったと。

二人は、たいそう年をとっていて、もう、歩くのがやっとじゃった。

それでも二人は、助けあって、なかよう暮らしておったと。

雨の降る日、いろりばたの二人の目の前に、雨もりのしずくがぽたり。

じいさんは、ばあさんにいうた。

「雨もりの穴をふさごうと思うんじゃが、体がいうことをきかん。すまんことじゃのう。」

「気になさるな。このままでええ。」

こんな調子で、とろり、とろりと毎日が過ぎていったと。

Baby Grandma

Once upon a time a very old man lived with his wife in a little house way out in the country. They were both so old and feeble that it was all they could do to make it through each day. But they were still very much in love, and by working together and helping each other they managed somehow to get by.

One stormy afternoon, as the old couple sat before their fireplace, the roof began to leak. *Plip. Plop. Plip, plop, plop.* Raindrops dripped steadily onto the floor beside them.

"You know," said the old man, turning to his wife, "I'd fix that leak if I could, Grandma. But I'm not as young as I used to be."

"Don't worry, Grandpa," replied the gentle old woman. "I don't mind."

二人は、このままなかよくお墓の中までも連れそって、いっしょに行くのじゃろうと、おたがいに思っておった。

ところが、思いもかけぬことがおこったんじゃ。

ある日のこと、じいさんが山へしば刈りに出かけたときのことじゃ。

「そうじゃ、ばあさまはきのこが好きじゃったな。とっていくか。」

ばあさまの好きなきのこを、じいさまはとっていってやろうと思いついたんじゃ。しばを背負ったまま、林の奥へ入っていった。

「はて……。」

いつのまにかじいさまは、道に迷うてしもうたんじゃ。道に迷えば気がせくし、おまけにその日は、かんかん照りの暑い日じゃった。

じいさまは、もうのどがかわいてたまらなくなったんじゃ。そんなじいさまの耳に、水の流れる音が聞こえてきた。

しげみをかきわけ下っていくと、小さな岩清水がわき出しているのをみつけたんじゃ。

And so it went. Life only grew harder for the old couple with each passing day, and they, in turn, became ever more dependent on each other. Both agreed that when the time came they wanted to die together. And they knew it wouldn't be very long now.

But then something happened to change all that. It started one morning when the old man was in the forest gathering firewood and spied some mushrooms.

"Grandma loves mushrooms," he thought. "Long as I'm here, I might as well pick some for her."

So, with his bundle of firewood strapped to his back, the old man shuffled slowly along picking up all the mushrooms he could find. Soon he had gone deeper into the forest than he'd ever been before.

"I guess that ought to be enough," he said to himself when he'd nearly filled his bag. "Now let's see... Uh-oh. Which way did I come from?"

The old man was lost. What's more, it was a very hot day, and he was terribly thirsty. Luckily, however, as he was wandering about looking for the path back home, he heard the sound of a waterfall. He followed the sound down a slope, parting the bushes as he went, and came to a little pool.

「おお、水じゃ、水じゃあ。」

じいさまは、ほっとして、
水に手を入れた。

「おお、つめたい。どれ、い
ただくとするか。」

じいさまは、水をすくって、ゆっくり飲んだ。それ
はまあ、なんとも甘い水じゃったと。

じいさまは、なんだかきゅうに元気がでてきたよう
な気がしたんじゃ。

もう一口、飲んでみた。一口飲めば一口だけ、体じゅ
うに力がみなぎってくるような気持ちじゃったと。

「う～ん、なんだか、元気がでてきたぞう。」

うれしそうなじいさまの顔が、ゆらゆらと水にうつ
っておった。

ところが、水にうつっているのは、若い男の顔――。
それは、若返りの水じゃったと。

　すっかり若返ってしまっ
たじいさまは、それでも、
まだ自分の身におこったふ
しぎには、気がついていな
い。

　それはそうじゃな、鏡が
なかったんじゃから――。

　元気いっぱい、もときた
道を帰っていったと。若返

"Thank goodness," said the old man, kneeling down and putting his hand in the water. "Oh! It's nice and cold, too."

He scooped up a handful and drank. How delicious it tasted! Suddenly he felt better than he had in years. He took another sip, and once again sensed a rush of youthful energy.

"Funny," he thought. "I haven't felt like this since I was a kid!"

The old man didn't notice his reflection in the rippling pool. But if he had, he would have been even more surprised. His face was now that of a *young* man. The wrinkles on his brow were gone, and his white hair had turned shiny black!

After taking one last drink, the man set out to look for the path home. This time he found it easily and headed back toward his house so full

ったじいさまは、たいへんないきおいで、家へ帰りつ
いた。

　さてさて、ばあさまが、どれほどたまげたことか。

　「いま帰ったよ、ばあさま。道に迷ってな、おそうな

ってしもうた。」

　戸を開け、入ってくる若返っ
たじいさまを見て、ばあさまは、
首をかしげた。

　「はあー、これはどこの若い衆
かいの。なんのご用ですかいの。」

　「なにをいうてる。ばあさまや、
わしじゃよ。」

　「はいはい、どこのわしですかいの。」

　「はて、昼寝でもして、ぼけとるのかいの。」

　「いいえ、わしゃ寝ぼけとりませんがの。ほんに、ど
このどなたさまかいの。」

　じいさまも、これはおかしいと思いながら、ばあさ
まのそばに寄っていった。

　「おい、ばあさまよ。わしじゃよ。おまえのじいさま
じゃよ。」

　「これよ、若い衆、じょうだんはいわねえもんだよ。」
と、手を振りながら、ばあさまは、ふと若い衆の着物
に目をやったんじゃ。

　「はて〜、これはたしかにじいさまの着ていたもんに
ちげえねえ。」

of pep and vitality that he was astonished by the change.

But that was nothing compared to the old woman's astonishment when her husband walked through the door.

"I'm home, Grandma!" he said. "I'm sorry it took so long. I lost my way."

The old woman cocked her head. "And who might you be, young fellow?" she asked. "What can I do for you?"

"What are you talking about? It's me."

"It's you, is it? You who?"

"Grandma, have you been napping again? Rub the sleep out of your eyes."

"I'm wide awake, young man. And I've never seen you before in my life."

The man was bewildered. He walked closer to his wife and said, "Grandma, it's me, your husband."

"Now look here, young fellow, if this is some kind of joke..." The old woman peered at the man. "Wait a minute," she said. "You're wearing Grandpa's clothes!"

「あたりまえじゃよ。わしがわしのもの着てて、どこがおかしい。」

「その声は、じいさまの声じゃ！」

「あたりまえじゃい。」

「はてえ、はれえ！　その顔はじいさまの若いときそっくりじゃあ！」

ばあさまの言葉に、じいさまははっとした。

「若いときとそっくりじゃと……。」

じいさまは、さっき山の水を飲んだときから、なにかへんな感じがしていたのを思いだしたんじゃ。

もう、なにがなんやらわからんようになって、たら

いに入れた水に自分の姿をうつしてみたんじゃ。

「ありゃぁ〜っ。ばあさま、こりゃいったいだれじゃあ。」

「わしも、わからんですじゃ。」

もう一度、たらいをのぞきこんで、水にうつった顔を見た。

「わ、わしじゃ。わしにまちがいない。わしが若返ったあ。あの水は、若返りの水じゃったのじゃあ。」

じいさまは、あまりのことに土間にしりもちをついてしもうた。

「ははは、若返った。くくく、若くなったぁ。ふわぁっ。」

"Of course I am. Why shouldn't I be wearing my own clothes?"

"That voice! That's Grandpa's voice!"

"Of course it's my voice."

"And that face. You look just like Grandpa when he was young!"

"When I was… young?" The man turned this over in his mind, remembering how wonderful he'd been feeling since he drank from the mountain pool. Finally, shaking his head, he went to the water barrel to look at his reflection.

"Oh, my!" he exclaimed. "Grandma, what's going on here?"

"Don't ask me!"

The man peered at his face in the water again. "It's me, all right. But how did I get so young? Wait… That pool I drank from. It… it must have been the fountain of youth!"

The man sat down on the floor with a crash. "Young!" he cried. "Ha, ha! I'm young again!"

じいさまは、大よろこびじゃった。そして、すぐに
ひょうたんを腰につけてばあさまにいうた。

「わし一人で若返ってはすまん。ばあさまにも若返り
の水をくんできてやるんじゃ。」

「それは、あしたの楽しみにしましょうよ。」

「ばあさま、あすまで待てる
かい。」

「待てますとも。年よ
りは気が長いで。」

「その年よりも、今
夜かぎりじゃ。」

若返ったじいさまは、
若者らしく、深く深くねむ
ったと。大きな寝息をたててな。

ばあさまのほうは、あすになれば、自分も若返れる
と思うと、うれしくて
なかなかねつかなかっ
たと。

夜があけて——、目
がさめたじいさまが、
となりを見ると、ふと
んがたたんであって、
ばあさまの姿はない。

「ありゃ、ばあさま、
ばあさま！

Suddenly he stopped laughing, jumped up, and turned to his wife. "But, Grandma," he said, "I don't want to be young all by myself. I'll go get some of that water for you, too." He found a gourd to carry the water in, and was heading out the door when his wife stopped him.

"It's late, Grandpa," she said. "Let's do it tomorrow. That'll give us something to look forward to tonight."

"You don't mind waiting till morning?"

"Heavens, no. If we old people know anything, it's how to be patient."

"Old? Not after tomorrow!"

The youthful Grandpa slept deeply that night. His snores echoed throughout the house. But Grandma was so excited by the thought of becoming young again that she couldn't sleep a wink. Finally she got up and crept quietly out of the house. And by the light of the moon she set off slowly along the path her husband had told her about—the path to the fountain of youth.

At dawn, the man awoke alone. When he saw his wife's futon folded up beside him, he realized she'd gone to look for the pool and chuckled to himself.

　ふふふ、行っただな。若返ってわしをびっくりさせる気じゃな。よしよし、わしゃ待つぞ。楽しみで待つぞ。」

　朝になるのが待ちきれんかったばあさまは、ひとりで若返りの水を飲みに山へ出かけたんじゃと。ゆうべのじいさまの話をたよりに、夜明けの道を出かけたんじゃと。じいさまをよろこばそう、びっくりさせよう、そう思ってな。

　じいさまは待ったと。いままでできなかった仕事を、若い体でどしどしかたづけながら、待ったと。

　いくら待ってもばあさまは帰ってこんかった。もう、昼もすぎたのに帰ってこんかったと。

　さすがに、じいさまは心配になった。

「道にでも迷ったんじゃろうか。」

　とうとう夕方になってしもうた。

　待ちきれなくなったじいさまは、山へ迎えにいったんじゃと。

　じいさまは、山道を走った。若返った体でぐんぐん走った。

「はて、赤ん坊の声じゃ。」

　あの岩清水の近くまできたとき、赤ん坊の泣き声が聞こえてきたと。

　なんと、見おぼえのあるばあさまの着物の中で、赤ん坊が泣いておった。

"Couldn't wait, eh? I guess she wants to surprise me. All right, Grandma. I'll be right here waiting."

To pass the time until she returned, young Grandpa fixed the leak in the roof and bustled about tending to all the other chores he hadn't been able to do before.

The day wore on but there was no sign of Grandma. By lunchtime, Grandpa began to worry. "Maybe she got lost," he thought.

Finally he decided he couldn't wait any longer. Convinced that something terrible had happened to his wife, he ran up the mountain path as fast as his young legs would carry him. He had almost reached the pool when he heard a noise and stopped.

"What's that?" he wondered. "Sounds like a baby crying."

He pushed on down the slope and through the brush until he came to the edge of the pool. And there he saw his wife's kimono lying on the ground. "Oh, no!" he cried. "Don't tell me she fell in!" He ran to the kimono and was about to pick it up when he jumped back with a gasp. Inside was a little baby girl!

　それは、まちがいなく、ばあさまじゃったと。

　なんと、じいさまをよろこばそうと、うんとたらふく若返りの水を飲んだばあさまは、若返りすぎて、赤ん坊になってしもうたんじゃ。

　じいさまは、赤ん坊をだいて、家にかえったと。

　それからのじいさまは、赤ん坊のせわで、とてもいそがしくなったということじゃ。

（おわり）

"G-Grandma?" whispered the man.

That's right. The old woman had been so eager to surprise her husband that she had drunk much more of the water than she needed. And the fountain of youth had done its work only too well. It had turned her into an infant.

The man picked his tiny wife up in his arms and carried her home. And from that day on, they say, he was as busy as a man can be, changing diapers, washing, cooking, and cleaning up after Baby Grandma.

おいてけ堀

　むかしむかし、あるところに、おいてけ堀とよばれるお堀がありましたそうな。

　このお堀には、こいやふながそれはそれはたくさんおってな、つり糸をたらせばいくらでもつれましたそうな。

　ところが、そのこいやふなをつって帰ろうとすると、お堀の水の中から、

　「おいてけ……、おいてけ……。」

という、きみのわるい声がしましたとな。

　「おいてけ……。」

という声がしても、魚を持って帰ろうとすると、その

Leave Them and Go

In a certain part of Edo, long, long ago, there used to be a canal full of big, hungry carp. All you had to do to catch these fish was to tie a hook to the end of a line and dangle it in the water. In a matter of minutes you'd have more than you could eat in a week.

As soon as you started home with your catch, however, a voice would call to you—a spooky voice that seemed to bubble up from beneath the surface of the water.

"Leave them and go," it would whisper. "Leave them and go."

If you were brave enough to ignore this and

声はだんだん大きくなって、ついには、

「おいてけっ！」

あたりにひびきわたる大声になりましたそうで。

そんなことが重なって、人々はこのお堀のことを、おいてけ堀とよぶようになり、だれもよりつかなくなりましたそうな。

ところがここに、なんとも気の強いとっつぁまがおりましてな。そう、商売は魚屋でありました。

「べらぼーめ、おいてけ堀がこわくて魚屋がやってられるかい。おもしれえ。おいらがつってこようじゃないか。」

女房やなかまがとめるのもきかず、お堀ばたにやってきたのです。

「おいらがこわがってるとおもってんな。ふん！おあいにくさまだい。ちっともこわかねえやい。ちょっといってつってくんからな。

いくぞーっ！」

と、けいきをつけて、土手をかけおりていったのでありました。

さっそくつり糸をたらすと、いや、つれるの、つれ

128

continue walking off with the fish, the voice would gradually grow louder and more insistent.

"Leave them and go!… *Leave them and go!*… LEAVE THEM AND GO!"

The fact that the canal was next to a grave-yard on the grounds of an old, run-down temple only added to the eeriness of it all, and anyone who ever caught fish there ended up throwing them back into the water and running for his life. Small wonder that over the years people learned to stay away from the place, which came to be known as the Leave Them and Go Canal.

One summer evening, a very stubborn and will-ful man came marching up to the bank of the canal. This man had a fish shop, and he was determined to return with as many carp as he could carry. Although his wife and his friends had pleaded with him not to go, he'd simply laughed at them.

"How's a man to make a living selling fish," he said, "if he lets some old wives' tale scare him off? Ha! Just watch me."

No sooner had he climbed down the bank and dropped his line in the water than he got his first

ないの、ほんのいっときの
あいだに、数えきれないほ
どのこいやふなが、わらわ
らとつれましたそうな。

　魚はたらいいっぱいにな
りました。

　「ざまあみろい。ぷっ。」

　とっつぁまは、家に帰っ
てから、魚をたあんとつっ
たうえに、おいらゆっくりたばこまですってきたのさ
──と、なかまや女房にじまんしたいばかりに、あせ
る心をむりにおさえて、一服つけましたそうな。

　でも、なぜか火をつけるのをわすれておりました。

　どのくらいたったでしょうか。夕方の鐘の音がひび
いてまいりました。

　「あはは、も、も、もうこんな時刻か。そろそろ引き上げ
るか。」

　魚がいっぱいのた
らいをもち上げて、
えっこらしょと、立
ち上がりました。

　とたんに、お堀の
水面がぶくぶくとあ
わだちはじめたので
あります。

bite. The fishing was every bit as good as he'd expected, and in no time at all he had two buckets full of big, tasty-looking fish.

"Ha!" he thought. "Wait till those cowardly friends of mine see this!"

He was about to head back home when he decided to have a smoke first. That would make an even better story to tell his wife and friends. "Afraid?" he could hear himself saying. "Why, when I'd caught all the carp I needed, I sat down right there on the bank and smoked my pipe!"

Smiling smugly, he put the pipe in his mouth—but, strangely enough, he never did get around to lighting it…

How much time had passed? The man himself had no idea until he heard the midnight bell tolling in the temple.

"What the… ? How did it get so late?" he wondered, putting away his unlit pipe. "I'd better be heading home."

He hung the two buckets of fish from either end of a wooden pole and hoisted it onto his shoulder. As he was about to start up the bank, however, the water in the canal began to bubble and boil, and a voice whispered:

　「おいてけー。」
　聞こえてきました。あの
声が……。
　どきっとするおとっつぁ
ん、耳に指をつっこんで聞
こえないふりをします。
　「おいら、なにも聞こえねえ。さいなら！」
　おとっつぁんははしりだしました。
　「おいてけえーっ。」
　はしるおとっつぁんの足が、宙にうきました。それ
でも、ひっしにはしって、土手をかけのぼりましたそ
うな。
　まだ聞こえます。
　「おいてけえーっ。」
　「うるせえや、うるせえ。なにがなんでも、女房やな
かまにこの魚を見せてやるんだい。はい、さいなら。」
　耳にせんをしたまま、おとっつぁんは土手の上をは
しりつづけます。
　おとっつぁんは、重い魚をかついで死にものぐるい
ではしりましたそうな。そして、やっとあのきみのわ
るい声が聞こえないところまできました。
　「べらぼーめ、おいらがつった、おいらの魚さ。おい
てけったって、おいていくもんかい。」
　ところが、そこへ、なにやら女もののげたの音が聞
こえてきましたそうな。

"Leave them and go…"

The man's heart stopped at the sound, but he plugged his ears with his fingers and pretended to ignore it.

"I can't hear anything. So long!"

"Leave them and go!" said the voice.

The man's knees were shaking as he scrambled up the bank.

"Leave them and go!"

"Shut up! I'm taking these fish to show my wife and friends, and that's all there is to it. Goodbye!" the man shouted, running along the top of the bank with his fingers still in his ears.

Struggling under his heavy load, he ran and ran until he could no longer hear the voice.

"Ha!" he gasped. "No old voice is going to scare me! I caught these fish, and nothing is going to make me leave them behind!"

He had slowed to a walk when he heard the sound of a woman's wooden clogs coming toward

からーん、ころん。

　からーん、ころん。

　その音は、だんだん近づいてきます。そして、やなぎの枝のところでぴたりととまりましたそうな。

　後ろにひけばおいてけ堀。前へすすめばきみのわるいげたの音。右と左はきゅうながけ。どうせにげ場がないのなら、前へいくほかありません。

　とっつぁまは、そろそろと歩きましたそうな。そして、やなぎの木をよけて通りぬけようとしたのですが——。

　やなぎの影にかくれていた人影が、すっと前へうごきました。

　やなぎの下からすがたをあらわしたのは、それはそれはうつくしい女の人でありましたそうな。

　「これ、その魚を、わたしに売ってくださいな。」

　女の人はやさしい声でいいました。

　「売らねえ！　女房やなかまに見せねえうちは、だれにも売らねえ。」

　とっつぁんがこういうと、女の人の態度がががらりとかわったそうな。

　「どうしてもいやかえ。」

　「う、売らねえったら、売らねえ。」

　「どうしてもかえ？　うふふふ……。」

　女は、とっつぁんのそばによって、顔を手でなでおろしたのです。

him. *Clip, clop, clippety-clop. Clip, clop, clippety-clop.* The sound stopped beneath a willow tree some distance ahead.

Behind the man was the Leave Them and Go Canal, and on either side of the road was a steep embankment. He had no choice but to walk on toward the willow tree, where the eerie sound of the clogs had ceased.

When he reached the tree, a shadowy figure stepped in front of him. The man froze in his tracks, petrified with fear, but just at that moment the moon came out from behind a cloud to reveal a beautiful young woman. What a relief!

"Please sell me those fish, sir," the young woman said in a gentle voice.

"Not a chance!" he said. "Not till I've shown them to my wife and friends!"

"You won't sell them?" There was something sinister about her voice this time.

"Absolutely not!"

"Are you sure?" she said with a ghastly cackle,

「これでもかえ
……。」
と、つき出した顔
は、のっぺらぼう。
「ふぎゃ──っ。」
とっつぁんは、
せっかくつった魚
をほうりだして、にげだしてしまいましたそうな。そ
のにげ方は、あとでおもいだしても、自分ながらはず
かしく情けないにげ方でしたそうな。

むちゅうでにげるうち、やっと夜なきそばの屋台の
明かりを見つけたのです。

よろよろとはしってきたとっつぁん、やっとのこと
で屋台にたどりついて、

「お、おやじ、水をくれ。水を……。」
というと、そばやのおやじが、後ろむきのままいいま
した。

「息をきらしてますね、おきゃくさん。」

「でたんだよ、あれが、あれが！」

「あれがじゃわかりませんよ。だが、もしかすると、
あれというのは、こんなやつじゃありませんでしたか
ね。」

そういいながら、ふりかえったおやじの顔は、これ
ものっぺらぼうでありましたそうな。

「ひ～～～っ。」

and she passed a hand over her face. "Even now?" she said, leaning forward.

Her face was as smooth as an egg—no eyes, no nose, no mouth!

The man let out a blood-curdling scream, threw his precious buckets of fish on the ground, and ran for his life.

On and on he ran until he saw the light of a noodle stall at the side of the road. He stumbled up to the stall, gasping for breath, and said, "Water! Please, give me some water…"

The man tending the stall had his back turned. "You seem to be out of breath, sir," he said. "Is something the matter?"

"I saw it! Back there, by the willow tree! I saw it with my own eyes!"

"It? What do you mean, 'it'?" said the stall keeper, slowly turning around to face the man. "Something like this, maybe?"

"Gaaah!" The man's knees buckled, and he fell flat on his behind. The stall keeper's face, too, was nothing but a smooth, featureless slab of skin!

とっつぁまは、こしがぬけてしまいました。

　いっぽう、夜なきそばの屋台は、おやじもろとも、ぺかりと消えてしまいましたそうな。

　こしをぬかしたとっつぁまは、しかたなく、はいずって、にげていったそうでございます。そのすがたも、あとでおもいだすと、死にたくなるほどはずかしいものでしたそうな。

　それでも、よろよろとわが家に帰りつきましたそう

な。

　やっとのことで家についたとっつぁまは、家にころがりこみました。

　「おや、おまいさん、へんな帰り方だねえ。」

　「べ、べらぼうめ。これがまともに帰ってこられるかい！　で、でたんだよ、あれが！」

　「あれが、じゃわかりませんよ。でもおまいさん、でたというのは、もしかして……。」

　女房がこういったときです。

　「も、もしかしたら、こ、こ、こいつもか……。」

　とっつぁまは、ちろっと女房のほうをぬすみ見ました。

The man was so terrified that his legs had turned to jelly, and he had to crawl away through the mud on all fours, gasping and whimpering. It seemed like hours before he made it to his house and somehow managed to pull himself through the doorway.

"What's wrong with you, dear?" said his wife. "Did you hurt your leg?"

"I saw it! I saw two of them!" he gasped, still on his hands and knees.

"Two of what dear? I don't know what you're talking about. Unless you mean..."

The man's heart froze. Slowly he raised his eyes to steal a glance at his wife.

"Unless," she continued, passing a hand over her face, "you mean something like—"

「もしかして、でたというのはこんなやつじゃなかっ
たのかい？」
　女房が顔をなでると、のっぺらぼう。
　「やっ、やっぱし！」
　どういうわけか、女房までのっぺらぼうになってし
まって、とうとう、とっつぁまは気を失ってしまいま
したそうな。
　とたんに女房のすがたは消えて、とっつぁまは、お
堀のそばの墓場でひっくりかえっておりましたとさ。

（おわり）

"No! Not you, too!" the man screamed, and fainted dead away.

And they say that when he came to, he was lying flat on his back… in the graveyard next to the Leave Them and Go Canal.

まんが 日本昔ばなし・妖しのお話
にっぽんむかし　　　　あや　　　　はなし

Once Upon a Time in *Ghostly* Japan

1998年6月10日　第1刷発行
2009年6月29日　第10刷発行

編　著　　　川内彩友美
かわうちまゆみ

訳　者　　　ラルフ・マッカーシー

発行者　　　富田　充

発行所　　　講談社インターナショナル株式会社
　　　　　　〒 112-8652　東京都文京区音羽 1-17-14
　　　　　　電話　03-3944-6493（編集部）
　　　　　　　　　03-3944-6492（営業部・業務部）
　　　　　　ホームページ　www.kodansha-intl.com

印刷・製本所　大日本印刷株式会社